Twisters, Braids and Cherry Pie

to Joshua,

Herb Marlow lives in Graham, Texas at this time. Born in Iowa, graduated from high school in Nebraska, married to Lynn (Loveland) Marlow in California, and owning a cattle ranch in Oregon, the author is widely traveled. In 1976 Herb and his family moved from Oregon to Texas. Dr. Marlow is a former pastor and a Ph. D. in Pastoral Counseling. He is also a former history teacher at junior high and high school level, and a sociology instructor at college level. Herb is listed in Who's Who Among America's Teachers, and Who's Who Among Human Services Personnel. Drawing on his experiences and his imagination, Herb has been telling stories all his life. He has for several years furnished stories and articles foe national periodicals.

Twisters, Bronc Riders, and Cherry Pie

By

Herb Marlow

Illustrated by

Julie Caffee

Ozark Publishing, Inc.
P.O. Box 228
Prairie Grove, AR 72753

Library of Congress cataloging-in-publication data

Marlow, Herb, 1940-
   Twisters, bronc riders, and cherry pie / by Herb
Marlow ; illustrated by Julie Caffee.
      p.s   cm.
   Summary: A young boy spends summers helping on
his grandparents' farm in Guthrie County, Iowa, and
there he learns the value of honesty, respect, loyalty,
and hard work.
   ISBN 1-56763-273-4 (cloth : alk. paper). — ISBN
1-56763-274-2 (pbk. : alk. paper)
   [1. Grandparents—Fiction. 2. Farm life—Iowa
—Fiction. 3. Iowa—Fiction.] I. Caffee, Julie, 1961-
ill. II. Title.
PZ7.M34525Tw 1997
[Fic—dc20   96-32100
                                                  CIP
                                                   AC

Printed in the United States of America

Inspired by

the late Arthur Paullin (Gramps), my maternal grandfather.

Dedicated to my mother, Vivian Simms.

Foreword

My Grandfather Paullin was a quiet, strong man—a farmer all his life. He raised five children on a forty-acre farm in the deep black loam of Iowa, then he elected himself to be a father-substitute to a small boy—me. Along with Grandma Paullin, my dog Jack, and all the farm animals, Gramps taught me about life. His values were simple but direct—total honesty, respect for others, loyalty, hard work, and always doing the right thing. This book is about my adventures on the farm and how secure I felt with Gramps always in the background. It is as much his story as it is mine. I loved and revered Gramps and hope that my life in some way reflects his.

Contents

One	Remembering	1
Two	Growing Hair	7
Three	Neighbors	13
Four	Hills Plowed Under	23
Five	Rescued	29
Six	Hayfield Medicine	37
Seven	Learning Respect	47
Eight	Cherry Pie	53
Nine	Snakes	59
Ten	The Days	67
Eleven	Quicksand	79
Twelve	Twister	85
Thirteen	Bronc Riders	93
Fourteen	Fishing	101
Fifteen	New Worlds	107
Sixteen	Old Jack	111

If you would like this author to come to your school for a storytelling presentation, please call (800) 852-7484

Chapter One

Remembering

The late Sunday afternoon sun was throwing long shadows through the elms when Gramps silently rolled off the old iron cot beneath the cottonwood and began to make his way to the wash house. I followed him as I had done all my memory life. It was chore time.

Things had changed little over the years. Gramps was a man of stolid habits; some might say he was stubborn to the point of dogma. We passed through the wash house, each picking up a waiting milk bucket. Morning and evening chores always began with milking.

I had tried many times to imitate Gramps's cow call, but to no avail. He would begin as soon as he entered the barnyard: "Cm-BOOOSSS! cm-BOOOSSS!" We could see the two milk cows in the small pasture. They were standing, waiting for the call. At the first sound, the large Guernsey led the way into the lane that ran between the hillside alfalfa field on their left and the oat field on their right. We entered the barn to put ground feed in the manger boxes.

Since he had moved from the cot, Gramps had not uttered a word. That was not unusual. Gramps seldom talked much and certainly not at chore time. His slow movements were deceptive; they accomplished much because there was no wasted motion.

1

I went to the gate to let the cows into the barn-yard. The gate was as always made out of strands of barbed wire, attached solidly to a deep-sunk fence post on one side, and fastened with a bale at top and bottom on the other. I pulled the pole toward the closing post, slipped the bale over the top, moved the pole out of the bottom bale, and pulled the gate out of the way of the opening, laying it on the ground.

"Leave it open," Gramps said from the barn door. "The horses are in the hill pasture." Still it felt odd not to close the gate behind the cows, so firmly had he instilled in me the importance of closing gates.

One of the milk cows was familiar. We named her "Bessie the Heifer" after a song that was popular at her birth. She would be seven years old now, having been born to old Blossom when I was ten. I remembered it well because it was the first time I had ever attended a calf-pulling. Bessie was that calf.

The other cow was red with a Jersey look to her head. She was an Ayrshire/Jersey cross most likely. She was smaller than Bessie and skittish, shying away from me as she came through the gate. "New cow?" I asked.

"Yep. Had her two months." Subject closed.

When the cows were in their stanchions, Gramps handed me a bucket and pointed to Bessie. I tucked the one-legged milk stool under my bottom and sat down on the cow's right side, pushing the bucket under her dis-tended udder. Grasping a teat in each hand, I began the

steady squeeze and pull that released the milk. It had
been a while, but the rhythm was still there.

There is really no sound like a stream of warm
milk jetting from a cow's teat to strike the bottom of a
metal bucket. "Pinnng, pinnng." I sighed with content-
ment. After a few minutes Gramps shifted his cud of J.T.
chewing tobacco and spat in the waste gutter that ran

just behind the cows, a sure indication that he was about
to speak. "You going to graduate?" There had been quite
a lot of doubt about that subject in the family. I had not
performed well in my last year of high school, staying
in trouble most of the year.

"Yes, sir. The principal told me I don't deserve to graduate, but he knows my mother, and she'll send me back until I'm thirty-eight—and *he's* had enough!"

"What will you do when you've graduated?"

"I'm going into the navy. I've already signed up and will leave a week after graduation."

Quiet reigned. Only the noise of chewing from the cows and the now changed sound of milk hitting a partially filled bucket: "Phuttt, phuttt."

Once again a stream of tobacco juice hit the gutter. "I don't suppose you'd want to come back and run this farm when your hitch is up?" An uncharacteristic wistfulness was detectable in Gramps's voice. Never had he asked me anything like this. How could I tell him that my horizons were about to expand far beyond the boundaries of Guthrie County, Iowa? How to explain my thirst for adventure? I let the silence lengthen until the time passed for an answer. But we both knew—I would never return to the farm.

Gramps chuckled and spoke in his quiet, remembering voice. "Remember that night when we pulled Bessie? You were just a pup."

"I remember. Grandma didn't want me to be exposed to things like birth and pain, but you said, 'Time he learned,' and that was that. It took me a while to figure out that you gave me the lead rope with instructions to loosen it if she went down just to keep me out of the way."

"You know, the old vet didn't want you out

there, either. It was his idea to give you the head. Sure made you jump when she bawled."

Quiet reigned again. Another stream of tobacco juice aimed at the gutter. Then, so quiet I almost missed it, Gramps said, "But you had to learn, Boy, you had to learn. I reckon there'll be a lot of calves pulled before you stop learning."

Chapter Two

Growing Hair

Looking back from that last visit before the U.S. Navy took me far away from the farm, I could see that Gramps's intention right from the beginning had been "learning." My parents had divorced when I was a baby, and my father moved out of the state. Since he was not around to provide me with a good male role model, Gramps elected himself to fill that void. He did a thorough job of it.

Mom, my two older sisters, Shirley and Janice, and I lived in the small Iowa town of Guthrie Center. Mom was a hard-working midwesterner of German and Scots-Irish descent who didn't believe in complaining about being left with three children to raise by herself. One of my earliest memories is of awakening in the night and going to the kitchen to find Mom ironing men's white shirts. Only later did it dawn on me that those shirts couldn't belong to us; she had taken in ironing to do at night for extra money. Gramps and Grandma reinforced in me the same work ethic they had taught my mother.

As often as possible I went to my grandparents' farm, a bit over four miles southwest of Guthrie Center. Town was okay sometimes, but overall it was the wide open spaces that attracted me. A forty-acre farm in the deep black soil of corn country might not seem like the wide open spaces to some, but to a little boy with no other experience, it was as large as the Panhandle of Texas.

Gramps was never a demonstrative man. He spoke little, but had a dry sense of humor that bordered on the hilarious at times. He loved to tell stories; some of them were even true. I loved to listen to his stories and at first always believed anything Gramps said. Later I learned to check with Grandma to see where the truth might lie.

My love for Gramps led me to hero worship. I closely inspected everything about him and tried to walk

and talk as if I were his clone. One hot summer day just before dinner (the noon meal in farm country) we were washing up at the bench outside the wash house. Gramps had rolled up his sleeves, and I noticed how much hair he had on his arms. Looking more closely I could see that his partially unbuttoned shirt displayed a lot of chest hair, too. I was not wearing a shirt so it was easy to compare my totally hairless arms and chest to his. "Gramps, how did you get all of that hair on your arms and chest?" I asked.

He looked at me with a twinkle in his eye (later I learned to be wary of that twinkle), spat out his cud of J.T., and rinsed his mouth with fresh water. "Boy, I'll tell you. When I was just about your age, I rubbed fresh chicken manure all over my arms and chest and let it dry. Pulled the hair right out." He turned and headed for the house.

My head was reeling as we sat down to eat. I could easily visualize myself with luxuriant hair sprouting from my thin arms and narrow chest. Grandma kept asking if I was all right and felt my forehead for temperature. She always thought I was sick if I showed any departure from my normal demeanor. I just smiled reassuringly. Gramps said not a word.

As soon as I could get away from the house after dinner, I ran to the chicken house. It wasn't a pleasant task I was set on, but Gramps had already taught me that often good things came from unpleasant beginnings. I smeared and smeared, trying to breathe only through my

9

mouth to cut the heady ammonia smell down. When I felt that I was well covered, I left the chicken house and stood out in the hot sun waiting for the organic hair grower to begin to work. That's where Grandma found me.

"What in the world do you have smeared all over you?" she demanded to know. I tried to explain to her that as soon as the elixir worked I would wash it off, but she wasn't in a listening mood. "Where did you get this idea?" she asked.

"Gramps told me that he put chicken manure on his arms and chest when he was about my age, and it made hair grow." She dragged me to the wash house and made me stand outside until she could heat enough water on the old wood range to fill the galvanized wash-tub. I was quietly pleased that it took her so long that the manure had completely dried by the time she plopped me into the suds. She scrubbed hard enough to remove a layer or two of skin along with the manure.

My memory picture includes myself being rubbed dry with a large towel, while Gramps leaned against the door jam of the wash house, roaring with laughter. Grandma was not amused at all.

Later that day, Gramps sat me on his knee and said, "Boy, don't you worry. I have a hunch that chicken manure treatment will work in time. Someday you'll have hair on your arms and chest." I was amazingly comforted by his words. And of course, like so many things he told me, this came true, also. By the time I reached my teens, I had a quite respectable growth of hair on my arms and chest. Now then, could it be that chicken manure had something to do with hair growth? Ah, the stuff that myths are made of.

Chapter Three

Neighbors

I vaguely remember a shepherd-type dog on the farm before Jack, but I must have been very young. Jack came to the farm as a young dog, and he and I grew up together. Gramps said we were pups at the same time. I loved Jack without limitation—and he felt the same about me. We were in agreement on almost everything, even our fear of thunder. When a fast summer storm came up, Jack would head for the wash house to hide under the wood range, and I would head for the house to hide where I could. The lightning wasn't really as frightening as the loud claps of thunder.

Another thing Jack and I agreed on was our dislike for a Pa Kettle-type neighbor who lived about a half mile from the farm. Hans was an anomaly in an area where there were many thrifty, hard-working farmers of Danish descent. His farm was always a mess of broken machinery, crudely patched fences, and straggling rows of corn, oats, and soybeans. Hans was always late planting his crops and late harvesting them. Only the deep-down richness of the black Iowa soil made it possible for him and his wife to survive at all.

Of course, Jack and I didn't really dislike Hans because he was lazy. After all, the word "lazy" didn't mean much to a little boy and a farm dog. What we took exception to was his smell. Hans never bathed, and he only changed clothes when something of the odd assortment that he normally draped on himself rotted and fell off. Grandma wasn't a dog lover, and she and Jack didn't see eye-to-eye on much, but they certainly agreed that Hans should stay on his own place.

I was playing out by the brooder house one morning when Jack raised himself from the ground nearby, the hair on his neck raised in a threatening manner, and he growled low in his throat. I had never heard him do that except when Hans was around. Sure enough, looking south across the ripening oat field, I could see what appeared to be a moving scarecrow, rags flying in all directions, moving much faster than Hans usually did. He was crying out, "Hhart, Hhart!" (Gramps name was Arthur, shortened to Art by his friends. Hans didn't handle English very well, and his version of Gramps's name always began with an "H.")

Gramps came from the barn where he had been repairing harness and waited beside me. Jack had disappeared. Hans staggered up and said, "Hhhart, them things has gone wild!" Of course, that's a hindsight translation of what he said. Hans was so excited and out of breath that his English was almost completely overlaid with Danish.

"All right, Hans, catch your breath and tell me what's happened." When Hans had calmed down a bit, he told Gramps that his horses had gone wild and kicked down the barn. They were still kicking when Hans

began his run to get help. Very quickly we were speed-
ing down the road in the converted Model-A Ford.
Gramps and Hans sat in the front, while I clung to the
side of the homemade pickup box installed in the back.
As hard as my seat was, I still didn't envy Gramps having to sit so close to Hans, who was almost visibly giving off waves of fear-and-exertion-induced rancid smell.

We arrived at Hans's place to see that the last of a falling-down barn was now a pile of rubble surrounding the two large pinto studs Hans called his team.

As in all other things, Hans had delayed having his horses castrated until it was far too late. Instead of having a team of docile geldings, Hans wound up with full-grown stallions—a source of constant trouble since Hans was terrified of them, and they knew it.

Gramps approached the wreck, carrying his "horse trainer," a two-foot-long piece of pitchfork handle that he had had around for a long time. He used it to prop the stable door open when he wanted the horses in. Though he called it a horse trainer, I had never seen him use it for that.

Before anything could be done with the horses, who had now settled down, enough splintered wood had to be moved to make a path to release them. Gramps and I did that ourselves, because Hans was too frightened to get that close.

Once two paths were cleared behind the horse, Gramps sent me a good ways off, then climbed over the debris in front of the manger. As soon as the studs saw him, they began to pitch and squeal. With no expression on his face, Gramps grabbed a halter rope, pulled that horse's head down, and whacked him solidly between the ears. The horse stood and trembled. Gramps untied the rope and climbed over the manger to back the horse out of the mess. He handed the lead rope to me, as Hans was hiding behind a large cottonwood tree. I'll never forget the thumping of my heart. Gramps gave me a long look and his small grin of courage. I took the lead and held on, trying not to look at the huge pinto looming over me.

In a very short time, Gramps had the second horse out of the wreckage, and both were tied to a stout tree limb. The three of us stood side by side to survey the remains of Hans's barn. "Hain't much left of ëer, is there, Hart?" Hans ventured.

"Looks to me like you've got enough pieces to make a lean-to, Hans. The boy and I'll come over tomorrow afternoon and give you a hand." I quickly looked up at Gramps, but he was wearing his stone face—the one he always wore when he didn't want anyone to know what he was thinking.

On the way home, I asked Gramps why we were going to wait until afternoon to help Hans. "We can put a lean-to together in half a day easy enough, Boy. We'll take our own tools."

"But why don't we go over in the morning, Gramps? Seems to me that we could have the work done before it gets too hot."

When Gramps didn't want to answer a question directly, he often created a riddle for me to figure out. "Your grandma is the best and cleanest cook in the county, Boy. Wouldn't want to miss her noon meal, would you?" I listened to his words, but didn't really understand their meaning until I asked Grandma later on. She explained that Hans's wife—known locally as

"The Old Lady"—was no cleaner than Hans. In addition, she was a terrible cook. Gramps would never say anything bad about anyone, not even Hans or his wife. Gramps's philosophy was that all people had good in them—some just kept it hidden a bit better than others. The bad could be overlooked most of the time if you were willing to give the good a chance.

The next afternoon we loaded the carpentry tools and headed for Hans's place. He was napping in a broken easy chair on what passed for his front porch when we arrived. I noticed that the horses were still tied to the tree. The piles of manure behind them told that they had spent the night there, although given the dilapidation of the other outbuildings, it was easy to see that there was no other place for them.

It was an interesting afternoon for a little boy. Gramps was polite to Hans and deferred to him in the matter of how the lean-to stable should be built, but he depended on me for help in the building. Hans was totally lacking in any skills with hammer and saw. Anything he attempted had to be done over. I was amazed at Gramps's patience and diplomacy. Of course, I spent as much time as possible up wind of Hans, trying unsuccessfully to avoid his odor. By midafternoon we had a solid structure erected over and around the huge mangers that had been constructed years before Hans bought his farm. The mangers were made of hand-hewn timbers and whipsawed oak. Gramps and Hans agreed that there was no need to try and move them. We just cleared the debris away and began building on that spot. By four o'clock, an open-front stable was up, roofed, and closed in on three sides. Hans had contributed a lot of talk, offers to help with no follow-through, and stains of tobacco juice on most of the boards I handled.

"Hans, there's enough lumber to close in the open side if you want. Probably a good thing to do before winter. You could even attach a milk shed. Of course, that's your decision."

"Thanks, Hart. I sure appreciate your help. I'll finish it up when I get time." Gramps didn't say what we both knew—if the open side was ever to be closed in, Gramps and I would come back and do it.

"Hart, you and the boy want to stay for supper? The Old Lady'll have something fixed pretty soon."

Gramps would have made a diplomat. He studied on the matter for a long enough time to appear to be considering it—certainly long enough to cause me some anxiety—then slowly shook his head. "Sorry, Hans, we sure appreciate the offer, but it's about chore time. Reckon we better go on home. You tell the missus we'll take a rain check, though. Hate to disappoint her."

On the way home, Gramps said not a word. I always tried to copy his silence, but it never worked. "Gramps, why doesn't Hans keep his place neat and clean like the other farmers around here?"

Gramps spat a brown stream of J.T. juice out the window and replied, "Boy, Hans is a grown man and can do things any way he wants. I want you to respect him because he is a man; but not everybody can be a good farmer. You're either born to it or not." He looked over at me with that twinkle in his eye. "Seems to me that you may make a pretty good farmer yourself someday." I always glowed under Gramps's rare compliments.

I was too young then to understand my grandfather completely. As an adult I came to know that he was not only fiercely independent himself, but extended that view of life to everyone else. To him, Hans had the right to live the way he pleased. Gramps would not ignore him or ridicule him as many of his other neighbors did. He would help him if Hans asked and never expect a return. And Gramps would defend to the end Hans's right to be just who he was.

Gramps's comment about me being a good farmer "someday" sort of made everything worthwhile, even Hans. Of course, that didn't mean that we had to eat The Old Lady's cooking.

Chapter Four

Hills Plowed Under

During the school year I had to stay in town, much to my disgust. I could only go to the farm on weekends and holidays. In the winter months when the snow was high and the air crackled with cold I didn't mind town so much, but at the first hint of spring my heart yearned for the country.

One long weekend in May when I was eleven, Gramps gave me a try at plowing corn all alone. Now for those who don't know, plowing corn doesn't actually mean plowing corn; it means to plow out the weeds between and around the hills. In those days, the corn in that part of the country was "checked" or planted in long, widely spaced rows that would look like a field of squares from the air. The spacing was important because a one-row corn cultivator pulled by a team had to fit between the rows.

The cultivator, called a sulky cultivator, was a strange-looking machine. The driver sat on an iron seat well back of center. The floating cultivator shovels were attached to wooden handles that jutted up above the wheels. Near the shovels were two iron stirrups. The object was to fit your feet into the stirrups, pass the tied reins over your back, and grasp the handles. While the team pulled the cultivator down the row, the driver swung the shovels in and out around the hills of corn, cutting the weeds away. At least, that's the way it was supposed to work.

I had been riding on the cultivator, even handling it some for several years. One morning, Gramps let me plow most of the time by myself, and I did all right. He sat under a shade tree and watched me, calling out instructions from time to time. At noon I pulled out of the field, and we headed for the barn, me driving and Gramps walking alongside. When I asked him if he thought I did all right, he just grunted.

Though I was not aware of it until grown, Gramps watched and analyzed me all of the time. As soon as I showed ability in some area, Gramps set up a test for me. Often I didn't know it was a test. I know now that he planned that, too, so failure would not make me want to quit.

When we reached the barnyard, we went about watering and unhooking the horses, then tying them in the shade with nose bags of feed. We washed in silence, then headed for the house and one of Grandma's tasty dinners.

After dinner, we took our usual noon rest. It was the custom in the country to sit or lie down for an hour after lunch. Not only did this rest allow the noon meal to digest, but it also made it possible to work a long afternoon.

When the time came to go hitch the horses back up, we did so again in companionable silence. I mounted the cultivator seat and clucked to the team. Gramps was at the gate into the lane, holding it open. When I had gone through, I stopped to wait for him to fasten the gate and walk alongside. He seemed to hesitate, then came on. We traded off that afternoon, each of us plowing for a while, then resting under the trees. Man, boy, and horses were all ready for chore time to come.

The next morning, after chores and breakfast, without being told I harnessed the horses and brought them to the plow, backing them into their places on either side of the long wooden tongue. Gramps came

from the wash house and held the gate, but when I looked back, he was on the other side of the fence. "You go on and plow in the creek-bottom field," he said. "I've got some things I want to do around here." And he turned and walked away. I was suddenly elated—and a little bit frightened. I had never plowed without Gramps right there close. But I knew that he meant what he said, so I headed the horse down the lane that would take us to the creek field.

At first, things went fairly well. I lined the horses up on the first row and fell into the rhythm of cultivating. Then I noticed that Bonnie was up to her old trick of letting Bell do all the work.

Bonnie was a spoiled mare that had been raised by my mother, aunts, and uncles. She was known to bite if you got too close to her mouth, and she was lazy, but very sneaky about it. She knew how to stop working while keeping the trace chains tight enough to appear that she was doing her share.

When I looked up and grabbed the reins with one hand to slap Bonnie on the rump, I got out of rhythm. I looked down to see small corn plants flying out of the rows rather than weeds. Letting go of the reins, I brought my feet and hands back into control, but then Bonnie slacked again. The rest of the morning went like that. Finally, I came to the end of a row and climbed done from the seat. Holding the lines tight, I walked up beside Bonnie and popped her one between the ears with a rein end as I had seen Gramps do. She jumped and tried to shy, but I held her tight. When she settled down, I got back on the seat and we tried again. For a while, things went better.

By noon I was exhausted. Bonnie and I had disputed who was boss several more times, and I was about ready to let her win. I decided that I would quit at dinner time and let Gramps fight that cantankerous mare in the afternoon.

Gramps was at the gate when I went in at noon. He helped unhitch the horses and water them. As he was leading Bell under the trees to put her nose bag on, he asked quietly, "Well, Boy, how'd it go? Have any trouble?"

This was my opportunity to tell him just how much trouble I had had. I opened my mouth, but all that came out was, "Yes, sir. You know how Bonnie always wants Bell to do the work. I plowed out some corn, but we finally decided who's boss." I was hoping he wouldn't ask how *much* corn, but he said no more.

All during dinner I wanted to tell Gramps that I didn't want to go back to that field, but I knew how he hated a quitter, and I just couldn't find the words. Oh, he wouldn't say anything, he'd just give me that special look that he reserved for those who wouldn't complete what they started.

When the meal was over we went out to rest in the front yard. I sat down on the grass, while Gramps was in his usual place, lying on the old iron cot. Neither of us said anything for some time, then Gramps spoke from under his hat: "Looks kind of like rain. Guess you better get back to the field. Be nice if you could finish today."

As I lined up for the first row I thought about the trust Gramps had placed in me. He might not have been so trusting if he had seen how much corn I plowed out, but I was determined to be worthy of his trust that afternoon.

The afternoon did go much better, and I finished the field, staying late to do so. Gramps had taught me two lessons that day: that I really could do whatever I set my mind to (his favorite bit of positive philosophy) and that it was always best to face your problems and try to solve them, rather than quitting.

Years later as an adult I happened to stand on the end of Gramps's old iron cot and look south toward the creek field. Suddenly I realized that I could see the entire field, and it dawned on me that Gramps had watched my whole sorry performance that morning so long ago. Yet, he had sent me back to the field that afternoon. He really trusted me far more than I had known at the time. He knew how important it was for me to learn lessons in life, and he was willing to sacrifice some corn to make that happen.

Chapter Five

Rescued

Learning to plow corn gave me a lot of satisfaction—and a bit of pain. One morning right after chores Hans drove his team and corn wagon into the barnyard. I held the team while Hans got down to speak to Gramps.

It was breakfast time, but I noticed Gramps —usually the most hospitable of men—didn't invite Hans in. I didn't know that Grandma had given an ultimatum: if Hans came in, she would go out and there would be no breakfast.

I could hear Gramps and Hans talking, but I didn't pay any attention to the words until I heard my name mentioned.

Now, I need to tell about my name. I had my father's name with a junior attached. I hated that name and always asked who gave it to me, but no one would really admit it. The first two names were bad enough—Herbert Clarence—but what really bothered me was the junior. My family had always called me "Junior." Gramps seemed to know that I didn't like it, and he rarely used Junior when speaking to or about me. He always called me "Boy." When I say I heard my name mentioned, what I actually heard was: "I'll send the boy over." I didn't say anything until Hans had managed to control his team enough to get them out of the barnyard and back on the road to town. Then, my curiosity got the best of me. "Gramps, I heard you tell Hans you'd send the boy over. What am I going to be doing?"

Gramps spat a brown stream on the ground, then said, "Those studs of Hans's got loose and tore his cultivator up. He wanted to borrow mine, but I suggested you go plow his corn instead. He agreed. You can start in the morning."

There was a lot left unsaid in that speech. Gramps never loaned machinery to Hans if he could keep from it, knowing that if he got it back at all it would be in pieces. Yet, he couldn't refuse to help a neighbor out. Neither could he go do the work himself, as that would be an insult to Hans as a farmer. But he could send me, a boy with little standing among men.

When Grandma heard what was to take place the next day, she didn't say anything, just looked at me with compassion. I didn't really know why she should be so disturbed. I didn't like to be around Hans because he smelled so bad, but there's only one seat on a cultivator, so I would be spared having to be too close to him.

The next morning Gramps suggested I leave before chores to get an early start, so I arrived at Hans's farm not long after daybreak. As I pulled into the lane leading to his house, I could see the remains of his cultivator tangled in the barb-wire fence of a small cornfield. Luckily, none of Hans's fields were large. The one I was to plow should be no more than a day's work for me.

It appeared that Hans and The Old Lady were still in bed. I didn't disturb them, just let down the sorry excuse for a gate and entered the field. Once lined out, Bonnie and Bell began the familiar pattern, and I fell into the corn-plowing rhythm.

It was well after eight o'clock by the sun when Hans finally appeared. He "whooped" from the gate, and I dutifully pulled up the shovels and headed in his direction.

Hans said, "Howdy, Boy. Wanted to tell you, in a couple of hours The Old Lady will have some coffee. When you hear me holler, come on in and rest your horses."

I really would have preferred to pass up the coffee, but I couldn't be impolite, so I thanked him and headed back to the field.

Midmorning came along with Hans's whoop, and I headed the team toward the gate. Leaving the cultivator in the field, I led the mares to the water trough, then tied them in the shade and made my way to the house, batting dust off my clothes with my hat.

Hans's house reflected the rest of his farm—ramshackle and falling down. One of the corner porch posts had rotted off, and the roof sagged almost to the ground. I circled this disaster and started to wash at the outdoor stand. Hans came through the screenless screen door looking as if he had just awakened. His smell preceded and followed him. In fact I had learned long before that it was almost impossible to get far enough upwind to avoid Hans's aroma altogether.

"Come in, Boy, come in." I did with reluctance. The Old Lady was standing at the range, pulling some rolls out of the oven. She was dressed in a feedsack frock as dirty as Hans's overalls.

"Sit down," she bellowed. I sat. Waddling across the uneven floor, she brought chipped coffee cups and dropped them in front of Hans and me. By this time I was trying to *not* breathe through my nose, but not very successfully.

The rolls looked good, but heavy. I took one when offered and placed it on the cracked saucer provided. The butter was growing rancid, so I passed that up, but there was a jar of store-bought strawberry jelly on the table, and I helped myself. The Old Lady poured strong black coffee into my cup and asked, "Do ya use cream?"

I did use cream in my coffee. Grandma's sweet cream was a delight in anything, particularly coffee. I answered in the affirmative. The Old Lady turned around and picked up a wash pan, then offered it to me. It was filled with cream which had naturally separated out of last evening's milk. Since the pan had not been covered, there was all manner of wildlife swimming in it. Now, I wasn't real squeamish, but the sight of large blowflies and a well-soaked wasp doing the backstroke in that cream about did me in.

Quickly I jerked my spoon back and said, "But I like it black sometimes, too."

"Suit yourself," she replied.

As quickly as possible I fled the house and went back to my clean-smelling team of horses. Once in the field I began to gloomily contemplate dinner served by The Old Lady. It was not a happy prospect.

Up and down the rows we went, turning the rich black loam. Almost before I knew it, the sun was reaching noontime. As I headed down a row toward the road, I saw Gramps enter in the Model A. A few rows later Hans whooped, and I headed for the gate. About half the field was plowed.

Gramps came to help me tend the horses, saying not a word. Hans stood by with his hands in his pockets. When we had them tied with nose bags on, Hans said, "Well, Boy, looks like you ain't goin' to get to eat The Old Lady's cookin' today."

I looked from him to Gramps. "That's right," he said, "I came to get you. You remember that pig that got away from us last week when we cut the rest? Well, I caught him today. Thought we'd take care of him, then you can grab a bite to eat at home before you come back here to finish up."

There were a lot of things I wanted to say. I even wanted to hug Gramps's neck, but that wouldn't do. With a conjured up look of disappointment, I merely said, "Yes, sir. Hans, please tell your wife I'm sorry I'll miss her meal."

When we were on the road, I said to Gramps, "You know, we could have just waited and castrated that pig when we do the other litter next week."

Gramps spat out the window. "Yep, reckon we could. But you know I don't like to put things off."

"Yes, sir."

The pig was waiting in a pen, and we finished that chore in about five minutes, then headed to the house. Washed up, I sat down to one of Grandma's fine noon meals of fried chicken, mashed potatoes, and apple pie. No one mentioned the food I was not eating at Hans's and The Old Lady's. And no word was said against that couple.

When the meal was over, Grandma gave me a huge butter-and-sugar sandwich, wrapped to take back to the field. Gramps only said one thing as we headed back to Hans's farm: "I ate The Old Lady's cooking once." Enough said.

That afternoon I made sure that I finished the field. It was late when I pulled back into our barnyard, but I was a contented young man. I was hungry, but I knew Grandma would have some more of her great cooking waiting for me, and I was content with knowing that I would not have to go back to Hans's the next day.

Chapter Six

Hayfield Medicine

Some of my favorite memories of the farm surround haying time. There was something really wonderful in the sun-warm days and scented air. I well remember when I was deemed old enough to help. As in all things, Gramps secretly watched to make sure that I didn't get into trouble, while treating me as if I were actually useful.

In those days, we used all horse-drawn machinery, the most dangerous of which was the mower. A hay mower was a two-wheeled cart with a raised seat and a series of gears that transferred power from one wheel to the sickle bar. The sickle bar extended outward at a right angle from the cart and was made up of a series of sharp sickle blades running back and forth inside a housing with stationary points. The bar was about six feet long. The danger involved was that the driver sat on the seat with no safety strap and handled the team by long reins looped around his back. A sudden jerk or a runaway could send him tumbling into the sickle. Obviously, Gramps did not allow little boys to drive the mower.

However, my first job in the hayfield was to walk ahead of the mower—far enough ahead to be safe—and pick up rocks that might break a sickle section. I collected the rocks in a feed sack and periodically emptied the sack at the foot of fence posts on the edge of the field. I was very proud to be entrusted with this important task. It never really dawned on me that the rocks I picked up were all very small and hardly likely to hurt the mower. Nor did I ever wonder about who picked up the rocks in the larger fields or when I was napping in the house. I just appreciated being included in the job of haying.

Once the hay was cut, it was allowed to lie on the ground for a few days to dry, then the team was hitched to the side-delivery rake and the next operation was begun. A side-delivery rake does just what its name implies; it rakes the hay together in a windrow and delivers it to one side, making long, winding snakes across the field.

When the hay was sufficiently dry, a pickup elevator was attached to the back of a hayrack (wagon) and pulled through the field, picking up the long windrows and depositing them in the hayrack.

As I grew older, I was given progressively more important positions in the hayfield. I graduated from rock-picking-up to horse feeder and hooker-up, then driver of the hayrack. By the time I was ten years old, Gramps was teaching me to "lay the hay about" in the rack. This was a very technical job, and I wanted to master it.

As the windrow of hay was picked up by the elevator, it proceeded up in a thick coil, leaving the mouth of the elevator in a considerable pile. One person always stood in the rack, balancing against the rocking of the hayrack, while distributing the hay in such a way that the rack filled evenly. A razor-sharp three-tined pitchfork was used to "lay the hay about."

The first day of my new duty went well enough. My loads were somewhat lopsided, but Gramps kept an eye on me and shouted instructions above the sound of the elevator. He also slowed the team at times to allow me to catch up. By the end of the day I was exhausted, but very pleased with myself.

When the hayrack was loaded, we would proceed to the barn where we must stack the hay. The hayrack was pulled alongside the front of the barn, beneath the huge, open hay door in the gable that led to the loft. Dangling from a track bolted to the extended roof beam was the hayfork. The team was unhitched from the rack and led around to the back of the barn where the horses were hitched to a large rope.

Gramps would climb into the rack and set the hayfork which was an upside-down U shaped with sharp points. Once he had pushed the fork as deep as possible in the hay, he pushed the spring-released clips in the inside of each tine that held the load together. Then he would call to the team on the other side of the barn, and they would begin to pull the load of hay up out of the wagon. As the load reached the roof-beam track, the wheel catch tripped and the hay ran down the track and into the haymow. When it was positioned where Gramps wanted it, he or I would pull on a long trip rope and drop the load. Gramps would yell at the horses to stop, then back, and we would pull the fork into position for another load of hay. Once the hayrack was empty, we would re-hitch the horses and go back to the field for another load.

On the second day of my new responsibility of laying the hay about, I suffered an injury not uncommon for that task. While trying to steady myself as the hayrack rumbled over a bump, and at the same time pre-pare for a sudden burst of hay from the elevator, I plunged the pitchfork into the hay. Unfortunately, my left leg was in the way. The end result was the center tine of the three-tined fork firmly embedded in the calf of my leg. I yelled to Gramps to stop, and he quickly saw my problem.

I always figured that Gramps could handle any situation that arose on the farm, and thus was not sur-prised when he also proved to be a crude, but effective, doctor. He removed the fork from my calf, pulled up my pant leg, and surveyed the damage. I was hard pressed to remain stoic, while unbidden tears carved trails in the dust on my face. "Is it bad?" I queried. "Naw, just a puncture. I can fix it," Gramps replied confidently. It was with amazed relief that I looked down on the hole in my leg slowly oozing blood. Gramps went to the tool-box attached to the front of the hayrack and brought back a roll of black friction tape. He took the wad of J.T. plug tobacco out of his cheek and slapped it on my wound. Oh how that tobacco juice stung! It took my breath away to the point that I couldn't yell. Then my hayfield doctor wrapped a half roll of friction tape around the leg to hold the tobacco in place. The first-aid station was closed for the day.

"You better drive, Boy. I'll lay about for the rest of this load."

I had sort of had the idea that we would go right back to the house and leave me there, but Gramps didn't seem too worried about my injury, so we stayed in the field until we had a load. This would be the last one of the day.

When we had unloaded the hay and taken care of the team, it was time to do chores. My leg was hurting a bit, but I only limped a little as we fed the stock and milked the cows. Later, when we went to the house, I'll admit I did limp quite heavily, but mainly to solicit sympathy from Grandma. However, I only wanted sympathy, not the fireworks that went off.

"What's wrong with your leg?" Grandma asked.

"Oh, I stuck the pitchfork in it a little," I replied.

"Let me see," she said. So I rolled up my trouser leg and let her see the wad of black friction tape. She had me sit on the edge of the table while she unwound the tape. What she found underneath brought forth such an invective that I wished heartily that I had never let her see.

"Dad, this boy has a puncture wound in his leg, and it's leaking some kind of brown blood!"

Gramps came in the house from the porch where

he had been changing to "house clothes" and took a look. "Oh, don't take on, Mother. That's tobacco juice. I put it there to kill the infection."

"Kill the infection? What infection? This boy is hurt, and you try to cure him with tobacco juice!?" I had never seen Grandma so mad before. Nor had I ever seen Gramps quail before another human being. He took one look at her face and beat a hasty retreat to the front yard.

Grandma began to practice her own brand of first aid on me then. I really liked Gramps's doctoring better, but I was wise enough not to say so. In fact, I didn't say anything at all except "Yes, ma'am" and "No, ma'am" the rest of the evening.

My grandparents always seemed very compatible to me, and I rarely heard a cross word between them. But they were as different as night and day. Gramps was a quiet, somewhat taciturn German, who had a dry sense of humor and was kind to most people. When he got mad I could only tell by the tightening around his mouth and the flash of his blue eyes. I had heard him get rough with stubborn animals plenty of times, but he rarely spoke harshly to me or anyone else.

Grandma was of a different temperament. She was of Scots-Irish decent, with red-gold hair and pretty white skin. I often went into the parlor to look at the pictures there, and the one that fascinated me most was a wedding picture of my grandparents. I believe my grandmother was eighteen when they married. In the picture, she was a beautiful woman. Even in later life,

Grandma was pretty. But when her Scots-Irish temper boiled, she was a woman to be avoided. This evening it was very close to boiling point.

Gramps evidently liked to live on the edge. Whenever he saw that Grandma was angry, he would goad her with a small smile. If she became vocal, he would laugh out loud.

"I don't know why you didn't bring this boy to the house when he was hurt," Grandma said. Gramps turned his smile on her.

"He could get blood poisoning from that pitch-fork, and what would Vivian have to say about that?!" Gramps began to laugh quietly.

"Mother, you know nothing can live through tobacco juice, and I applied it right away. The boy is fine. He'll be a bit sore in the morning, but I'll bet it won't affect his appetite."

"You think he's just like another one of the animals. Maybe we better just take him to see Doctor Todd tomorrow."

Now that made me nervous. In those days people rarely went to a doctor unless they were very sick. Farm families particularly would provide their own brand of medical attention, then wait to see what happened. Only in extremity would they actually call a doctor or go to see one. In some ways seeing the doctor might have been an adventure, but I knew Doctor Todd, and I wanted no part of him.

There may have been other doctors in Guthrie

Center, Iowa, when I was a boy, but I don't remember any of them. Dr. Todd was our family physician. He was a rough, easily exasperated man. I'm sure that he was a competent medical man as well, but the only time he saw me, he seemed to always feel it necessary to give me a shot. And for some reason, it was always in the bottom!

Actually, Grandma was only trying to worry Gramps, but it only worried me. "Do you think it's bad, Grandma?" I asked.

"Well, it doesn't look too bad, but we'll want to keep an eye on it." Grandma could see that she had worried me, and she didn't really want to do that. "Now, don't you worry. I'm sure it will be all right."

The next morning my leg was sore, but I could walk okay. When Grandma unwound the bandage, there was no angry swelling or redness which I knew was associated with blood poisoning. She pronounced me fit enough to do light work, so I went back to the hayfield with Gramps. However, in deference to my weakened condition, he allowed me to drive the hayrack while he did all of the laying about.

Later that day an event happened that pushed all of my worries over wounds and blood poisoning aside. By midafternoon we were hurrying the team down the lane to the barn. Great thunderclouds had suddenly appeared in the southwest, heralding a storm.

In that part of Iowa, sudden thunderstorms are not uncommon in the summer. The clouds would boil up in the afternoon or evening, and lightning would begin to flash. Great peals of thunder would crash as if the world were coming to an end. Then rain—and sometimes hail—would pound down and the wind would blow. Sometimes these storms would spawn tornadoes (called "cyclones" in that part of the country) which would sweep the country with destruction. Usually the storms did not last long, but their results might be long in recovering.

The clouds had been piling up for some time when we headed for the barn. Gramps wanted to have the hay and the team under cover before the storm hit. Quickly we positioned the hayrack under the fork. I unhitched the team and trotted them to the other side of the barn, while Gramps set the fork on the load. He told me to stay with the horses, as they were becoming nervous by the change in weather. Three sets of the hayfork, and the load was off. I began to unhitch the horses just as the first drops of rain were falling.

Suddenly, a huge shaft of lightning split the sky. I felt the jar as it struck a tree some distance away. The thunder sound was so loud it almost knocked me over, and the horses began to squeal and pitch, trying to run. I knew I was not going to be able to hold them, when Gramps suddenly appeared at their heads. He grasped a bridle in each strong hand and led the team toward their stable. Still skittish, they moved into the familiar stalls, and we tied them up.

The rain was pelting down now, mixed with a few small hailstones, not large enough to do any damage. Gramps and I stood at the open door of the stable and watched. He looked down at me with that quiet grin of his, spat a brown stream of tobacco juice, and said, "How's your leg, Boy?"

I started and looked down, then pulled up my pant leg. The bandage was soaked—as was every stitch I had on—but the leg looked fine. "Looks okay, Gramps. I reckon I can lay about now."

Gramps began to chuckle, looking at the rain pouring down. "By the time that hay's dry enough to work, you won't even have a scar left."

It was true that my leg no longer bothered me by the time the last of the hay was dry enough to put in the barn, but I did have a scar—still do, as a matter of fact. That J.T. cud and black friction tape sure worked though, for I never had any problem with blood poisoning.

Chapter Seven

Learning Respect

In my family, respect was taught from baby-hood. Children were taught to respect adults, other people, property, the law, God, and each other, not necessarily in that order. Talking back to a parent would bring a quick punishment, because talking back was a mark of disrespect.

Gramps taught me a lot about respect. He particularly taught me about respecting women. I know that in today's world many women don't want any special treatment. I recently heard about a law against using foul language in front of or directed to a woman or "female child" being stricken down by the North Carolina Supreme Court. The argument was that females were no more sensitive than males and should not be protected by law from foul language. Gramps would not have approved that decision.

Gramps did use strong language at times. When he worked animals, he would sometimes swear at them, or he might say something off-colored when he hit his finger. But he would never use bad language in front of a woman. Further, he would not allow anyone else to use bad language in front of a woman. He proved that to me one day in town.

In the days I'm writing of—the late 1940s and

early 1950s—it was a tradition for farm families to shop in town on Saturday afternoons. I particularly looked forward to this time, even though the town we went to was my hometown of Guthrie Center. One reason I liked to go to town was because I always got a dollar from my grandparents, and a dollar was a lot of money in those days.

This particular Saturday, we arrived in Guthrie Center about 2:00 P.M. We went first to the creamery where we left the cream cans and egg cases. (Gramps was paid in cash, and that was the only cash I ever saw him receive. My grandparents were frugal and never went to the bank for money as some farmers did.) Then we parked the shiny 1941 Dodge on Main Street. Grandma headed for the Super Value Grocery, and I tagged along, knowing where I would find Gramps later on.

The way I always received a dollar on Saturday evolved from my grandparents' ideas about money. I was taught that you never told anyone how much money you had, nor did you confide how you spent your money. Money was a very private matter.

After leaving the car, I only followed Grandma for a short time, for I really didn't enjoy going grocery shopping. As soon as she secured a cart and entered the first aisle in the store, she stopped and began to search through her purse. Finally she turned to me and said, "Here's fifty cents. Now, don't spend it all in one place and remember to save some—and don't tell Grandpa I gave it to you."

"Yes, ma'am," I replied, and sped away.

Finding Gramps on Saturday afternoon was no trick. He always began his time in town sitting in front of the pool hall, visiting with his cronies. Sure enough, as I rounded the corner, there he was, surrounded by other farmers in town for the day.

My Gramps was a man of presence, though I didn't understand that until I became an adult. In any gathering, Gramps was always the acknowledged leader. Not because he tried to assert his authority, but because other men naturally and instinctively recognized it. Gramps didn't talk very much, but he would listen with interest to anyone who spoke to him. When he did speak, other men always listened with attention.

When I arrived the men were all discussing something new that the government was proposing—the Federal Land Bank. Gramps was not saying anything, but the others were divided in their opinions. I hung on the fringe of the group until Gramps looked up and grinned at me. He got up from the bench and led me around the corner. "Here's fifty cents. Now don't spend it all in one place. Wouldn't hurt if you saved some. Don't say anything to Grandma about this."

"Yes, sir, I sure will, and no, sir, I won't." These were the words I always used. With a twinkle in his eye, Gramps went back to the discussion, and I headed for the drugstore to load up on peanuts and bubble gum.

I ran into my cousin and best friend, Jerry, as I was coming out of the drugstore. Jerry and I always tried to spend time together on Saturday. Sometimes we would go to the afternoon movie, or we might just walk around town. This particular Saturday we walked to my house on 4th Street, not far from downtown. I showed Jerry the new treehouse I had begun to build before going to the country. He was properly enthusiastic. We didn't spend much time there though, because both of my sisters were at home. They always had things they wanted me to do, and I never wanted to do them, so we quickly headed back to town.

Jerry didn't have any money on this Saturday, so I shared everything I had with him. He would do the same if he was flush and I wasn't. My dollar ran out pretty fast.

We walked on over to the group of men still talking in front of the pool hall. Jerry's dad, my Uncle Willard, was there along with Gramps and the others. Uncle Willard was as quiet as his father, so the two of them were not saying much. I noticed that one of my least favorite people had entered the conversation. His name was Harold, and he was a loud, bombastic know-it-all. To my knowledge, Harold had never been a success at anything. He had a "chronic" back injury that conveniently kept him from working, and he lived with his widowed mother. She had a small pension which she evidently shared with Harold.

Harold's lack of ambition did not make him well liked in a community of hard-working people, but he seemed oblivious to scorn and contempt and was quick to hold forth on any and all subjects if given the chance. I have often marveled at the tolerance shown by the farmers who would allow him to enter their circle.

Today, Harold had become an expert on farm subsidies and was well into a loud and profane speech on "those crooks in Washington," when a farm wife walked by on the sidewalk. One of the men nudged Harold to quiet him, but Harold just looked at the woman and let out his vilest oath.

I had never really thought about my grandfather as a dangerous man, nor a quick one. He moved so swiftly, it was almost as if he vanished from one spot and reappeared in another. I saw him grab Harold by the shirt front and with a tremendous heave lift the bigger man right off his feet. Harold sat down hard on the sidewalk, looking up at Gramps.

"Harold, you'll go apologize to that lady about your language, then you'll stay off Main Street on Saturday afternoons from now on." Gramps's voice was deceptively quiet, but the strength and authority rang like a clear bell. Harold began to nod his head.

"Yes, sir, Art, I'll do that. Can I go right now?"

Gramps didn't say any more, just went back and sat on the bench. Harold got to his feet and quickly walked after the woman, calling to her to "please stop."

From then on, I always looked for Harold when we went to town. One Saturday afternoon I saw him come out of the dimestore as I was headed there to spend the best part of my dollar. But when he saw me, a frightened look came over his face, and he almost ran to get off Main Street. When I mentioned it to Gramps, he only grunted.

I've never forgotten the lesson I learned about respect on that Saturday afternoon. Even in early adulthood when my language was not all it should have been—particularly after several years in the navy—I could never use curse words in front of women. Now, when it has been years since I have used strong language at all, I am often shocked by the words I hear *from* women, let alone the words men and boys use in front of them. Gramps's lessons still survive.

Chapter Eight

Cherry Pie

July was upon us and it was hot. I loved the long hot days and the sudden thunderstorms. The corn would be high and green in July, and driving to town was like traveling in an open-topped green tunnel. August was a month away, and I didn't dwell long on the fact that early in September, after Labor Day, I would have to return to school. July was a great month in my calendar.

On one hot early July afternoon I was lazing away under the huge cottonwood in the front yard, lying on Gramps's cot and reading my way through a large stack of already-read-several-times comic books. Gramps was tinkering in the shop, and Grandma was listening to "As the World Turns" on the radio. I could hear the radio voices through the open dining-room window, though the words were made indistinct by the heavy curtains.

My eyes turned to the loaded pie cherry trees just outside the fence on the south side of the yard. I liked cherries. I would often go by and pick one or two to pop into my mouth, but never more than a few, as Grandma had impressed on me the need for all of the cherries to go into green or clear quart fruit jars. In the winter she would make cherry pies and serve up dishes of cherries at dinner.

Still, I thought about those cherries. Gramps encouraged me to keep the birds away from the trees, and I worked at that from time to time. Hadn't I earned a good bait of ripe cherries right off the tree? I convinced myself that I had.

Without thinking too much—I didn't want to kick my conscience into action—I got up from Gramps's cot and climbed over the wire fence. Working on the back of the tree, I started pulling cherries off the tree and stuffing them in my mouth, spitting pits at the ground. I was sneaky enough to know that I needed to spread out my picking so that a large gap in the crop didn't give me away. Finally, after an hour or so, I had had enough, and I slipped back over the fence into the yard.

Just before chore time, Grandma came out of the house with a dishpan and went through the gate and began to pick cherries. "Need some help, Grandma?" I queried.

"If you want. I'm going to make a pie for supper." Wow! Hot cherry pie fresh out of the oven! That was very near to heaven to me. I quickly scaled the fence and began picking. Of course, I had to eat a few of the plumpest cherries right off, but that was permissible when picking for a purpose.

When Gramps and I began to pour the fresh produced milk into the separator, we could smell the cooling pies (Grandma always made at least two pies at a time, though she usually spoke of only one) that sat on the kitchen windowsill.

There was a normal system to eating meals, and it had to be followed. Though I would have liked to eat pie right off, first the main course had to be dispensed with. That wasn't really a big problem, because Grandma's meals were always good. This particular supper contained pork chops, fresh corn-on-the-cob, boiled potatoes with the skins still on, gravy made from the skillet the chops were fried in, and large, crusty rolls. I managed a generous helping of all.

Finally, the moment of truth was before us. Grandma cleared a spot on the table and placed a warm cherry pie there. Gramps took the carving knife and sectioned the pie. Then he scooped one fifth of that ambrosia into a deep dish and set it in front of me.

I will admit that I was very full by the time I addressed the pie, but I had a reputation of being a big eater at any time, so I pulled a deep breath and began to eat. The pie was everything it appeared to be. Each bite released the wonderful flavor of cherries and light crust. When I finished I literally could not have managed another bite. In fact, I was so full that breathing was a bit of a problem.

We always went to bed early on the farm. The thirty-two-volt electrical system was fine for the few electrical objects it ran, but even though the basement was filled with storage batteries, too many electric lights would quickly deplete the source. Our habit was to use lights to clean up the kitchen, then move into the dining/living room, turn off the lights, and turn on the radio. We would then all sit in the dark and listen to those wonderful radio programs; "Amos and Andy," "The Great Gildersleeve," "Fibber MaGee and Molly," and more.

This particular night I began to feel a bit queasy in the stomach about halfway through Fibber and Molly. I knew that if I went to bed early, Grandma would think I was sick and would give me one of her home remedies, probably castor oil. UGH! So I toughed it out until the program was over, and Gramps began his going-to-bed ritual.

I was tired from the day's activities and fell asleep quickly, but I awakened after midnight with a roiling stomach and a terrible headache. Slowly, I crawled out of bed and made my way to the slop jar. (Slop jars have mercifully passed from the modern scene, but in the days before indoor toilets, they were a necessity in every bedroom.)

Grandma heard my retching and came into the bedroom. When she saw what was happening, she went to find a wet cloth to wipe my mouth and forehead. We both knew that the cherries of the day, including her delicious cherry pie, had become the problem of the night. After an hour or so, my stomach finally settled down enough that I could go back to bed.

The next morning I was very weak and shaky. Grandma wanted me to stay in bed, but I persuaded her to let me lounge in a chair in the living room.

Gramps didn't actually laugh at me, but he had that tight little grin on his face, and the lines around his eyes had deepened. He only made one comment. At lunch, I was eating Grandma's chicken soup while he addressed boiled beef and potatoes. Gramps looked at me with that twinkle in his eye and said, "Good thing Grandma made two of those cherry pies. I figure you'll be ready for a piece as soon as you finish your soup, right?"

My stomach turned at the thought of eating cherry pie or even cherries ever again. He saw the look on my face and took pity on me. "That's all right, Boy. Now you know why I don't care much for rhubarb pie. Had an experience about like yours."

As always, Gramps knew just the right thing to say to make me feel better. By late afternoon I was feeling good again, but I avoided the cherry trees from then on, and I never have cared much for cherry pie since.

Chapter Nine

Snakes

The oats were golden in the field, and Gramps began to oil the McCormick Binder. Combines were becoming more and more popular with farmers for harvesting oats and other small grains, but Gramps was always slow to adopt new things. He still harvested his oats in the way he always had, cutting them with the binder, stacking the bundles in shocks to dry, then gathering the oat bundles to a central location where the threshing machine stood. Oat harvest took place in the hot, hot summer. I had always loved harvest time, but this year would be special because I would, along with my same-age-cousin Jerry, be allowed to actually work with the men.

I learned to drive the binder, while Gramps stood the bundles up in shocks. Then we would trade off, and I would shock the bundles. Now shocking is a skill that must be learned. A shock is started with a bundle sat upright, pushed firmly into the stubble of the field. Other bundles are leaned against the center one and stacked two high into a small sloping hill of grain that gave some rain protection. The trick was to make the shocks strong enough to stand any amount of wind. I soon learned to be a good shocker.

Once the field was cut and shocked, threshing

could begin. Gramps and Uncle Willard had a threshing machine that both used. Gramps had fewer oats to thresh, so they decided to take care of his first, then move the machine to Willard's farm. We would all work on both farms. A couple of neighbor men were also going to help.

A threshing machine is an awesome monster The huge separator looks like a square dinosaur. The large straw blower flue looked just like a giant neck. The threshing machine had been a marvelous invention when it was first developed. The bundles were pitched

onto a conveyor, the twine that held them cut, and the grain-head-capped straw disappeared into the gaping maw. Inside, the grain was separated from the straw, grain being conveyed into a waiting wagon through a spout, and the straw blown out to pile up some distance away. Threshing machines were noisy and dirty. Oat chaff and dust filled the air around the machine, landing on sweating faces and trickling down necks to itch and burn. In the past, one of my jobs had been to clean up around the threshing machine. I would pitch loose and dropped bundles onto the conveyor or oil the many bearings. The year before when I had had that job I learned to my dismay just how noisy the machine was.

Jerry and I had been talking about chewing tobacco. We had both tried some, but felt that we were old enough now to become serious about the dirty habit. I began taking small amounts of J.T. out of the pocket of Gramps's bib overalls, which he conveniently hung on a kitchen hook. I always suspected he knew I was taking his tobacco, but he never said anything.

By threshing time that year, I had gotten past the sting and had begun to keep a small "chaw" in my mouth when I was out working around the farm. We were several days into the harvest and had fallen into a routine. One afternoon I was cleaning up around the conveyor, facing the machine. I had just put a fresh chaw in my mouth and was working it around to a comfortable position, when I felt a tap on my shoulder and heard Grandma's voice in my ear telling me that she had a cheese sandwich and a glass of iced tea for me. I froze in position.

It was common at harvest for the women to bring out a midafternoon snack and drink, as the men would often work until eight or nine o'clock at night with no other food after the noon meal. I was not surprised at Grandma being there. I just didn't want her there at that time. What could I do?

Before I turned around I quickly swallowed my cud of J.T., then I turned and grabbed the tall, cold glass of iced tea, gulping it down, trying to put out the fire trailing down my throat. The tea hit my stomach a few milliseconds after the tobacco, but they both came back up together. I was instantly sick and vomiting. Over the sound of retching I heard Grandma say, "If I've told you once, I've told you a hundred times—don't drink that iced tea so fast when you're hot!"

Out of the corner of my eye I could see Gramps bent over and slapping his knee with glee. He knew exactly what had happened. That ended my interest in chewing tobacco, though Grandma never knew it.

But that was last year. This year I was released from those dirty chores around the thresher, giving them willingly to my younger cousin Bobby. Jerry and I were to have a team and hayrack of our own.

The first day dawned hot and dry. Just at daylight Jerry and I left the barn headed for the oat field. We were using Gramps's team of mares, Bonnie and Bell. When we reached the portion of the field that we had been assigned, we pulled the rack between two shocks and got down. The horses would respond to voice commands so that both of us could load the hayrack.

Jerry was on one side, and I pitched from the other for the first layer. It was important to get this layer positioned correctly, as it would be the foundation that kept the load from sliding off. Oat bundles are very slick and will slip and slide around if not anchored securely.

Once the first layer was on, one of us had to climb onto the load and carefully place each bundle. We decided to trade off, with Jerry on top first. I would keep the horses moving and pitch up the bundles.

When the rack was half full, we changed places. We were proud of our work and felt that this load would be the best-looking one in the field. Just as I had completed the fourth layer, the horses pulled one hayrack wheel up over a rock. As it dropped off, I was off balance and threw my pitchfork into the load at one edge. The load shifted and began to slide as Jerry yelled, "Look out!" and most of it slid right off the rack. We had a mess on our hands now. Gramps saw us and came over to help put things right. "Boys, you've forgotten to turn each layer so the butt is against head, that's why it fell. That's okay, everybody has to learn. I'll help you put it right." We felt a bit let down, but we were glad for Gramps's help. When he left we went back to work, making sure that we stacked our hayrack in the right way.

By midmorning, we had delivered several loads to the thresher, and we were feeling cocky again. Jerry was on the load, working on the third layer, when I had an inspiration. Reaching down to lift a bundle, I noticed a bull snake slither under another. Now bull snakes are not poisonous, and in fact are helpful in the oat shocks as they eat mice who love to eat the oats. But a snake is a snake, and seeing one unexpectedly always brings a moment of fright. There were rattlesnakes around, and we had to be careful of those.

Working very carefully, I gathered up the bundle the bull snake had crawled into and with a quick heave sent it toward Jerry, yelling, "SNAKE!" as soon as it was in the air. Jerry didn't hesitate, he left the hayrack as

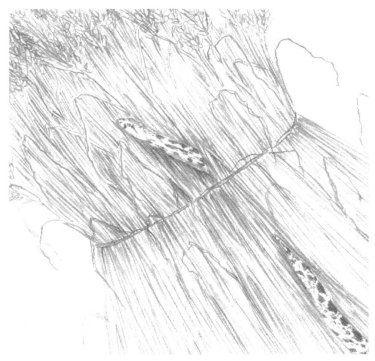

quickly as possible, throwing himself over the side and taking a good portion of the third layer with him. I was laughing and slapping my knee when he tackled me, and the fight was on. Luckily, none of the men saw what we had done, and as soon as Jerry cooled off a bit, we put the load back together. Of course, the rest of the morning we would occasionally call, "SNAKE!" when we threw a bundle, just to keep the guy on top worried.

Noontime finally arrived with Jerry and me as hungry as only two growing boys can be. Of course, even if we hadn't been hungry, a harvest meal in those days was something to look forward to. The farm women tried to outdo each other in preparing to feed the threshing crew. The results were always beyond description.

There were always several kinds of meat—beef, pork, chicken, even game birds at times. These were accompanied by mountains of potatoes, huge ears of fresh corn, great bowls of rich gravy, hot rolls, and slabs of fresh-baked bread. For dessert there were cakes and pies like nothing you can find in a store today.

Gramps whooped loud and long, signaling dinner time, and we all headed for the barnyard with our teams. Of course, the horses had to be taken care of first. They were unhitched and led to the water tank for a short drink, then tied in the shade of the huge elm trees with nose bags in position filled with ground feed. Finally, we all washed at the pans set out by the women, then headed for the house.

Dinner was ready, but Jerry and I knew it wasn't

ready for us yet. The farming families in our area all followed the same procedure when feeding a large number of people: the men ate first, followed by the women and children. Eating with the men was a privilege that had to be earned, so Jerry and I resigned ourselves to sitting on the porch with the younger children, while our stomachs growled for the food our noses told us was nearby. Perhaps we would get lucky and Grandma would slip us a biscuit covered with butter and sugar.

We could hear the shuffling of feet and chairs as the men were seated and the mumbled blessing. Things grew quiet. Then we heard one set of footsteps headed in our direction. Gramps's stocky form filled the doorway behind us. We looked around as he bellowed in a loud voice, "What are you two men doing out here? We aren't going to wait all afternoon. Come in and eat!" and he turned back to the dining room.

When we walked into the room and took the two seats waiting for us, all was quiet. The men gathered there all wore large grins. Perhaps they were remembering when they had first been included with the men. Those things may not be important anymore, but Jerry and I will never forget that graduation.

Chapter Ten

The Days

Fishing was a great pastime and recreation for many farm families. My Uncle Willard and Aunt Marge were real enthusiasts. They would often include me in fishing expeditions, and I appreciated it. Of course, if the fish weren't biting or the adults wanted to stay too long, we children would become bored and often get into trouble, but that was part of the scene.

There were no clear mountain streams in the Iowa I knew. Most fishing was done on the large and dirty rivers or the many lakes in the area. Even farm ponds could often be good places to fish.

The equipment we used would not delight a fly fisherman, nor even a modern stream angler. Often the car would sprout long cane poles. Or if a rod and reel happened to be used, it was usually a heavy, clumsy affair, designed to handle the large line necessary for river-bottom angling.

We used different bait in those days, too. Large nightcrawlers could be picked up off the ground after a hard rain filled their holes. These huge fish worms would often extend to over one foot in length. We would collect nightcrawlers and keep them in gallon cans filled with damp earth. Of course, regular fish worms, smaller but even more plentiful, and fat white grubs were also popular. These could be dug out of the ground in areas around gardens or outbuildings.

My favorite bait was found in grocery stores, though not sold as fish bait. We called it "store-bought bread." In other parts of the country, it's known as "light bread." Since most farm women of the day made their own bread, for many of them it was a treat to buy the weak, tasteless stuff that town women used. The problem was, most of the men refused to eat the produce of a mass-market bakery. However, they had no problem with using it for fishing.

We prepared this bait by opening one end of the package and pushing a hand down through the loaf itself, squeezing and shaping as we went. The result was a large dough ball, suitable for pinching off pieces to mold around fishhooks. Catfish were particularly fond of dough balls, and on a good day a treble hook packed with dough would entice the large fish that inhabited the bottom of lakes and rivers.

One Friday evening Uncle Willard and Aunt Marge came over with their three children, Jerry, Lila, and Bobby. Jerry and I were best friends as well as being cousins. Uncle Willard was my mother's brother. Jerry and I tolerated Lila as a girl because she was often willing to play boy-games: cowboys and Indians, cops and robbers, etc. She would even take minor parts when necessary. But Bobby, being the youngest, was only a pest. We spent our time when he was around either trying to hide from him or making him miserable enough to go away. Of course, Bobby had no compunction about telling on us, so we often got into trouble for teasing him.

On this Friday my uncle and aunt proposed to take me home with them that night and then fishing with them all day Saturday. Gramps and Grandma gave their permission, so I was released.

It was always exciting to go to Jerry's house. Aunt Marge was not the world's greatest housekeeper, but she ranked near the top as a mother. I loved the casual way things "happened" at Jerry's house. Meals were always fun, because Aunt Marge herself never really knew what she was going to have until she started fixing it. We might sit down to a wonderful feast of fried pork chops, leftover chicken, a pot of beans, and fresh lettuce from the garden. Or it might be radish sandwiches and roasting ears. It didn't really matter, because we would always have a lot of laughter as a side dish.

Aunt Marge has always been very special to me. She and I both loved to sing, and we often sang together. She called me "Bing" and I called her "Rosie" after that great pair Bing Crosby and Rosemary Clooney.

Another thing I loved about staying with Jerry and his family—they would make a freezer of ice cream at anytime. No special occasion was necessary. And I loved homemade ice cream, especially Aunt Marge's maple flavored. Uncle Willard and Aunt Marge were a hard-working farm couple, but they also believed that people should have some fun. No farmer could predict or change the weather, but many tried by worrying about it. Uncle Willard seemed to know that worry wouldn't change things, and while I'm sure he did worry at times, he didn't sit around and stare at the walls in gloom. It was better to take his problems to the riverbank.

Saturday morning after chores we all piled in the old Ford and headed for the river. There were poles poking out of every window, and we were all as excited as if we had never before gone fishing. When we arrived, we parked the car on the edge of the road and made our way down well-packed paths to the low riverbank.

There were many ways to fish the rivers of Iowa. Some people had small boats they carried on top of their cars. They would move out into the middle of the river and trail lines. Other fishermen would string "trot lines" across the river at narrow spots. These were long heavy ropes or lines with short fish lines attached trailing baited hooks. These trot lines were often left for days and presented quite a hazard to other fishermen.

We fished from the bank, using cane poles with strong, black line tied to the end or rods and reels. Kids could hold onto a pole and watch a cork bobber that held the line from sinking to the bottom. When a fish decided it liked the bait offered and bit, the bobber would be pulled under the water, letting the fisherman know he had a fish.

Adults and older children used fishing rods with reels attached. They could cast far out into the river and either let the hook drop to the bottom or attach a bobber.

One danger involved in fishing was that of hooking something other than a fish. We had only been fishing a short time when I whipped the line from my pole back over my head and attempted to shoot it as far as possible into the river. But the line didn't follow the cast. Instead, I heard a yelp behind me and looked back to see cousin Jerry at the end of my line. I had hooked him in the left arm. Luckily, the hook was not very sharp and had only embedded itself lightly in Jerry's skin. Uncle Willard was able to remove it without resorting to his pocketknife.

I always had another problem when I went fishing—my skin was light and I sunburned easily. I will never forget the day I spent in a boat fishing on a lake with another uncle—Verl—and his wife, Lois. I had been swimming in the late morning and sat in the boat with only swimming trunks on for several hours. When I finally felt the burn on my legs, it was too late. For several days I was unable to wear long pants, while large yellow blisters formed on both legs.

After hooking Jerry, we decided to quit fishing

and explore the riverbank. We didn't find any treasures like lost knives or treble hooks, but we did sit and talk with a young man who said he was a hobo. Now this fascinated us, as we both secretly yearned for the open road. Not only that, but the hobo was smoking hand-rolled cigarettes, just like Uncle Willard. He could even roll them with one hand. He offered the tobacco and papers to us, but we made a lumpy mess of our efforts.

After a while we went back to where the family was to find something to eat. Aunt Marge's wonderful lunch was waiting for us. The long, happy Saturday ended as dusk began to creep up the riverbank. We loaded our gear and ourselves into the Ford and headed home to do chores and fall into bed.

The next morning, Sunday, we all went to church in town. That is, Willard and Marge took me along with their family; we stopped and picked up Grandma on the way, and Gramps waved us away from the front yard. I'm sure Gramps must have gone to church at some time, but I don't remember the occasion. When I asked him about it, he would only grunt and avoid answering.

The church that we all went to—that is, all the family that lived in or around Guthrie Center—was First Baptist. There were many unique things about this church, not the least of which was the pastor. This man—we'll call him Reverend Wilson—did not like children and made no bones about it. He did like Chihuahua dogs, and he had several. Of course, the children knew that he didn't like them, and they, myself as leader, took every opportunity to tease his dogs.

All of our ministers had not been like Reverend Wilson. There was one named Reverend Blood, who was a fine man, concerned about his family and his parishioners. Reverend Wilson seemed only concerned about himself.

As we arrived at the church that Sunday morning, I noticed my mother and sisters waiting on the church steps. I was a bit worried that Mom might want me to come home rather than go back to the country, but that was not her purpose. She wanted to let us all know that there would be a church picnic that afternoon at the city park. Since she was aware that Aunt Marge had not heard about the picnic and so had no food prepared, Mom said she had made enough for both families.

Jerry and I immediately began to make plans for the picnic. In Sunday School we were a bit more subdued than usual, whispering to each other. Our plans surrounded some kind of attention to Reverend Wilson and his dogs.

The morning church service was always a difficult time for children. The sermons were long and boring, and children were not invited to take part. I'll never forget the hush that fell on the congregation one morning when a visiting boy about my age rang out a resounding "AMEN!" at some point in the sermon. The poor boy was rushed from the church by his embarrassed parents.

We began by hearing the Sunday School report, then sang hymns—my favorite part of the service. After announcements and offering, Reverend Wilson took his place behind the pulpit. He had already warmed up with a long, long prayer, so he was ready to go. Preachers of those days were long on bombast and short on theology. Reverend Wilson liked to preach against "things" and other people. One of his favorite subjects was the Methodists and their "wrongness" in being baptized by sprinkling rather than dunking. Though he never actually said it, I certainly picked up the idea that if a person was not baptized in the right way, there was no hope of going to heaven. This was one thing that prompted me to go forward for salvation and baptism during a revival at the tender age of nine.

Another of Reverend Wilson's favorite topics was the evil of tobacco. However, he was wise enough to know that he had a very narrow window to work in. After all, most of the deacons either chewed tobacco, used snuff, smoked cigars or pipes, or rolled their own cigarettes. That left only one form of tobacco that the good Reverend could rage against—tailor-made cigarettes. Cigarette companies had been making these paper-wrapped tubes of tobacco for a long time, but among the farmers of our area they really hadn't caught on too well. Perhaps that was because they were expensive—often costing as much as twenty cents a pack.

When Reverend Wilson got the tailor-made cigarette bit in his mouth—no pun intended—he could easily keep the words flowing for over an hour. The deacons all sat and nodded at every charge, knowing that their own habits were safe. Of course, the few men (no one ever suspected any of the women of smoking, though I knew of two of them who did secretly) who regularly bought and smoked the "evil weeds" squirmed a bit, but that just stoked the fires of Reverend Wilson's furnace.

As well as being a long-winded preacher, Reverend Wilson was a marathon-class eater. He had an imposing paunch and was not adverse to adding to his girth with the good cooking of the women of the congregation. However, most of the women didn't like him and certainly didn't care for the way he spoke about their food.

Reverend Wilson had a habit of taking a bite of whatever he happened to capture, then saying in his loud voice, "My, that's MUSTY," then, after a pause, "I MUST eat some more." He evidently thought he was complimenting the woman who had prepared the food, but they didn't see it that way.

At one church supper he learned that his favorite comment wasn't so popular. He had just taken a large bite of a piece of golden-crusted apple pie when he launched into his spiel. Just as he completed, "My, this pie is musty," the good woman who had baked it grabbed the dish out of his hand and said, "Then don't eat it!" The laugh was certainly on Reverend Wilson, who had no sense of humor when the he was the subject of the joke.

Church was finally over, and we all headed to the city park for the picnic. Jerry and I had made our plans.

The city park was a lovely place to picnic. A small creek ran on the west side, and huge trees were spotted across the grass, leaving large enough openings for ball games. There was a city swimming pool in the park, but we rarely had an opportunity to use it, as there was a small charge to get in. Also, recently a sinful pavilion had been added—a skating rink. I never could figure out why roller skating in a rink was sinful, when almost every kid in town had steel-wheeled roller skates that they could use on the streets and sidewalks. Of course, Jerry and I had long before determined that adults set the rules on sin, and for the most part anything that was fun that they didn't want to do was sinful. Simple theology, I'll admit, but it satisfied us.

As we had expected, Reverend and Mrs. Wilson brought their Chihuahua dogs to the picnic. They tied them on long leads in the shade of a tree near their car, a huge Nash that looked like an upside-down bathtub on wheels. Our plan had depended on this arrangement, so we were glad to see things going our way.

The ladies all began to unload and uncover the food they brought, placing it on the picnic tables provided by the city. When all the dishes were opened, and flies for several miles around had been summoned by their fellows, one of the ladies said to Reverend Wilson, "Reverend, would you pray, please?" He had never passed up the chance yet.

For some reason Reverend Wilson's meal-time prayers were even longer than his church prayers. Perhaps he was repenting beforehand for the amount of food he was about to consume. At any rate, when he had closed his eyes and held up his clenched fists to begin his sermon-prayer, and the rest of the crowd had their eyes closed, Jerry and I slipped away. We crept behind the Wilson's huge blue Nash and untied both dogs, then spooked them into running. Now these dogs were yappers, so they yapped at every occasion. As we tossed small stones at them, they gave voice.

Well, the prayer ended without an "Amen." Suddenly, Mrs. Wilson heard her babies and saw them running free across the park. She didn't see Jerry and me because we were hidden behind the Nash. When everyone was concentrating on trying to catch the dogs, we slipped into the crowd and chased along with them.

Later, when the Chihuahuas had been corralled and retied in plainer view, Reverend Wilson began to question the children to see who had committed the sacrilegious act. None of the children would admit anything, not liking Reverend Wilson anyway. Some of them probably saw us, but nobody told on us. The adults didn't say anything, just let Reverend Wilson go on with his interrogation.

On our way home that afternoon Uncle Willard said a funny thing. Jerry, Bobby, and I were sitting in the front seat with him, while Grandma, Aunt Marge, and

Lila were in the back. Uncle Willard looked over at Jerry and me and said, "I always wondered just how fast those yappers could run myself," and he had that same twinkle in his eye that Gramps did from time to time.

Chapter Eleven

Quicksand

A small creek ran near Gramps's farm, sort of curling around through the Baileys' property, then touching our fields on the south border. This was a wonderful place to explore, and I went there with my dog Jack as often as possible.

Jack had a phobia about guns that was difficult to overcome. No one really knew why he was afraid of guns, but there it was. He had evidently been frightened by a gun being shot near or at him when he was a pup, because the sight of a gun, or even the noise of thunder, frightened him.

Now, Jack wasn't a hunting dog, so being afraid of guns would not normally have been a problem. However, to me he was all dogs wrapped up into one, and I wanted him with me when I went "hunting."

Of course, I didn't hunt with a real gun, but I had a Daisy repeater BB gun that was the next best thing. I began training Jack to accept this gun by tying him to my belt by a short rope, then firing the gun in the air. At first he pulled and tried to run, but after leading him around for several hours, Jack finally learned that the sound of the gun wouldn't hurt him.

After a time, when I picked up the BB gun and called Jack, he came with enthusiasm. We would then head out through Burdet Bailey's cornfield, across the road and east of our farm. When the corn was tall, it was quite an adventure to move through the rows of tall stalks. Sometimes we would flush a pheasant or a covey of quail. Occasionally we found a deer bed, but rarely did we see a deer. Raccoons were common along the creek-side edge of the field, and there were always plenty of cottontail rabbits.

Jack was happy at chasing and barking at these animals who inhabited the cornfield. By the time we reached the rough pastureland around the creek, his tongue was hanging out a yard. He would always leave me as soon as we emerged from the corn and head directly to the nearest water hole.

Brushy Creek (pronounced "crik" in the Midwest) was a small, meandering stream fed by springs and draining a considerable area. When heavy rains came, the creek would run bank high, and it was dangerous to wade in. But at other times—most of the time—the stream of water was narrow enough to jump across and shallow enough to wade at almost any point.

The creek ran generally south, parallel to the road for quite a distance, then it made a sharp turn to the west, crossed under the bridge a quarter mile south of Gramps's driveway, and wound off across the country. Just west of the bridge the creek had gouged out a deep hole. This was a spot that all of the kids in the area utilized as a swimming pool.

There was one problem with the swimming hole—quicksand. Due to the floods that often sent the creek out of its banks, the deposits of quicksand changed locations from time to time. Usually there was a spot somewhere around the pool, and we would check for it by probing with a long stick.

I had planned to swim today and took my clothes off as soon as I arrived, splashing in the shallow end (unless girls were around, we boys always swam naked). Jack liked the water and came with me. He didn't do much swimming, but his coat was so thick he loved the cool of the water and often found a hole to submerge himself, leaving only his head above.

I had picked up a long dead limb to use as a pole and slowly began to work my way into the deep part of the pool, probing as I went. I found one point where the stick went down in a steady, sinking manner that told me it was quicksand and quickly moved away. I guess that gave me false confidence, and I quit looking from then on.

Paddling around in the swimming hole was a

81

real "cool" thing to do on a hot summer day, and soon I was enjoying myself. I had actually taught myself to swim—well, dog paddle—in that pool without anyone knowing. Gramps had told me that he had learned to swim by pushing a wide board in front of him and kicking with his feet. As always, anything Gramps told me had to be tried, and I had quickly learned that the board worked. By now I no longer needed the board and felt quite safe in the water.

Snakes could sometimes be a problem around the swimming hole. No one had ever seen a cottonmouth (water moccasin) there, but we always kept an eye out. I had just crossed the pool and was preparing to climb out on the bank when I heard the dry slither of a snake. Without trying to find out what kind it was, I quickly backed into the water and headed for the other side.

The side of the pool I swam to had a very steep bank. The other one, where the snake was, was a gentle slope and always used by swimmers. I stopped at the high bank and looked back for the snake while I continued to dog paddle. The water was deep here, and I didn't know if I could stand or not. I was just a bit panicky, but I tried to control that.

I couldn't see the snake, and I was growing tired. I decided to put my feet down and see if I could touch bottom, then I would walk around the edge of the pool and reach my clothes from the other side of the snake. I was delighted to find that I touched mud and sand almost immediately. I could stand, with water only coming to my waist. I took a step. My foot sunk and was gripped by cold and clammy sand! I tried to pull it out, but it only went deeper. Then the other foot began to sink! "QUICKSAND!" shouted in my mind. I was caught in a pocket of quicksand!

I knew that I shouldn't struggle. That would only make me sink faster. But it was hard not to try and pull my feet loose. Yet, I still sank slowly and inexorably. "Jack! Jack!" I called. He had disappeared. "JACK! JACK!" I screamed. Jack heard the panic in my voice and appeared on the opposite bank almost immediately, whining.

Maybe if I could get Jack to swim over, I could hold onto his coat, and he could pull me out. "Here, boy. Here, Jack," I called as calmly as possible. He slowly entered the water and began to swim my way. But I was still sinking. The water now came to my chest, and I could feel my feet being sucked deeper and deeper.

Jack was coming, almost where I could grab him, when my feet hit solid ground. A great feeling of relief swept over me. I hugged Jack and let him lick my face. "It's all right, boy. It's all right." I began to work my legs back and forth, slowly breaking the suction of the quicksand. Jack wanted to swim away, but I held onto him. Between us we managed to pull me out, and we swam together back to the other bank. I crawled out and flopped on the grass beside my faithful dog, no thought of the snake that had so frightened me before. I was alive and safe. What a wonderful feeling!

As we moved across the road and entered the front gate, Grandma was just going up the back steps. "Did you two have a good time this afternoon?" she asked. I grinned, and Jack wagged his tail. "Sure did, Grandma. We sure did," I replied. Long ago I had learned that it was wiser not to share all of our adventures with grownups. If Grandma knew about my brush with death in the swimming hole, she would naturally forbid me to go there again. Now that I knew where the quicksand was, there was no reason to worry, was there?

Chapter Twelve

Twister

Every farm in our area had a storm cellar. Most of them were dirt-floored holes in the ground, though a few like our neighbors to the north—the Rasmussens—had an elaborate cellar with a concrete floor and electric lights. Ours was the former variety. Not only that, but the water table was so near the surface on our farm that the floor was almost always covered with water.

Gramps used the storm cellar as a vault. Hanging from the chicken-wire ceiling was a collection of wire-handled lard buckets, each one full of some sort of papers. Jerry and I had pulled one down and opened it one time, but we couldn't make any sense out of what we found. Only later did I learn that the lard buckets were full of war bonds purchased during the Second World War as part of my grandparents' contribution.

I believe that our storm cellar had a concrete floor, but I never really investigated it that closely. Even on the occasions when the water went down, the floor was covered by oozing mud that might have felt good to bare feet out in the daylight, but in that dark cave, everything was spooky.

Grandma was very afraid of storms. She had a dishpan struck out of her hands when she was young,

85

and it had quite naturally left her with a fear of the wild storms that could suddenly spring up on a summer day or night.

Many times Grandma would awaken me in the night with the words, "Come on, Junior, a storm is coming, and we're going to the cave." Gramps didn't usually go on these midnight journeys, and when I discovered that, I began to ask if he was going before I committed myself. If Gramps didn't go, I preferred to stay in bed, but if he was going, I knew it was a bad one, and I would quickly dress and head for the shelter.

One afternoon, about two o'clock, Gramps and I were working on a fence up by the hill pasture when he stopped and looked at a large dark cloud in the southwest. "Come on, Boy, let's get on back to the house."

"Why, Gramps? We can finish this fence in a little bit, can't we?"

"Yep, we can. But if that cloud over yonder has in it what I think, it won't matter much whether this fence is fixed or not. Let's go."

I looked at that boiling, sinister green-black cloud and quickly loaded the tools on the wagon. Usually Gramps walked the team wherever he went, but today he lashed them into a fast trot. We bounced into the barnyard and quickly unhitched and stabled the horses. The stillness of a few minutes ago had been replaced by a strong southwest wind, blowing cold out of the cloud. As soon as the team was taken care of, we ran for the storm cellar. Grandma was already there. As we ran through the wash house, I could see just the tip of Jack's tail curled around the leg of the cooking range there. He always crawled under the stove when a storm came.

There must have been six inches of water covering the floor of the cave, so none of us went all the way in. Grandma was on the bottom step, I was about midway up, and Gramps stood at the door. Now the door didn't close firmly, as the frame had warped. Our cellar had a regular kitchen door set in a sloping entrance. The door faced east because storms rarely came from that direction. Gramps wanted to watch the cloud, so he had to lean out of the door and look past the hump of the cave.

"What's it look like, Gramps?" I asked.

"Well, it's big and sure has a lot of lightning in it. I reckon there's a twister in there somewhere."

Suddenly, rain and hail began to pound down. Gramps jumped back into the entrance and pulled the door shut behind him. Now the sound of the rain was drowned out by the howl of the wind. The sound grew and roared, like a huge train bearing down on us. The hair on the back of my neck was standing up, and my eyes must have been huge. Gramps sat on the second step, holding the door closed and trying to look calm, but somehow I knew that he was scared, too. I had never before seen Gramps afraid of anything.

I looked down at Grandma. She tried to smile at me in reassurance, but it was hard. The wind sounded louder, then seemed to quiet a bit. Slowly the sound abated. Gramps stood up and looked out a crack in the door, then he pushed it open a bit and looked out. Rain was still pounding down, but there was no hail. We waited as our hearts returned to normal beating.

When we finally emerged from the storm cellar, we were amazed to find little damage. A big limb had blown off the cottonwood, and there were smaller branches all over the place, but the house was unaffected. We did find a lot of dead birds, and the water had washed out some of Grandma's plants. When we went through the wash house, Jack slowly emerged from under the stove, looking sheepish and wagging his tail for understanding. I stopped to pet him, and he was suddenly himself again.

The barnyard was littered with branches and dead birds—some of our chickens among them. The chicken house had suffered more than any other building. A large limb had blown into the front, breaking out the windows and knocking off a corner of the roof. However, everything else was standing unharmed.

In the cave it had seemed that the cyclone was passing directly over our heads, but as we looked south we could see that we were actually on the northern edge of the storm. Later, we learned that Casey, Iowa, had been hit by the full force of the cyclone and two people had died there.

The next few days we spent cleaning up from the storm. All of our livestock was okay, with the exception of some fifteen chickens. We cleaned up all of the dead birds and repaired the chicken house. Gramps even climbed the cottonwood in the front yard to cut the stump of the broken limb. We felt very fortunate to have escaped the force of the storm.

On the third day after the storm, Gramps and I headed the Model A down the road to Hans's place. "Gramps, does Hans have a storm cellar?"

Gramps spat a brown stream of tobacco juice out the window and thought a moment before he spoke. "Boy, you've got to remember that Hans means well, but he doesn't always get things done. Several years ago he started a storm cellar, but he didn't get very far. I offered to gather up the neighbors and help him dig—like we all do for each other around here—but he was mad at the Schlosses and the Baileys and didn't want any help. Well, I respected that and didn't press him. The cellar was never finished." I still marvel at the tact my grandfather used when speaking of his neighbors. Hans was too lazy to finish digging his storm cellar and too stubborn to let the neighbors do it. So he didn't have a storm cellar. As far as Gramps was concerned, he had the right to be that way. End of subject.

When we arrived, I looked around to see if I could find any destruction caused by the storm. This was not easy, because Hans's place usually looked like a cyclone had just gone through. Hans came out of the house to greet us and invited us in. Gramps declined, saying we were just passing by and wanted to know how he and "the missus" survived the storm.

Hans cackled, showing the brown snags that he called teeth, and slapped his leg. "Hhart, it was the funniest thing I ever see. The Old Lady was outside when the storm hit. She run in the house, but it was creakin' and groanin' to beat the band, so she run back out. I'm out here watchin' the cloud, and she yells at me, 'Get under cover, ya old fool!' I says, 'Where?' but she was gone, runnin' to the chicken house.

"Course the chickens was blowin' all over the place, and The Old Lady was tryin' to catch 'em. Wasn't havin' any luck, either. About the time I got there to help, she had the rooster under one arm, and she was arunnin' for the stable.

"Next thing I know it starts to rain and hail. I headed for the stable myself and crawled under the manger. You know how stout that manger is. I looks around and there's The Old Lady, holding on to that rooster for dear life.

"Well, when the storm was over, I crawled out and helped The Old Lady up. She's hangin' onto that rooster, got him clamped under her arm, head backward. 'At least I saved the rooster,' she says. I reached out to take it from her, and that rooster was dead! She'd clamped him so hard under her arm that he suffocated. I laughed, but she was sure mad. Stick around for dinner. We're havin' what's left of that old rooster!"

Of course, Hans kept lapsing into Danish, so he didn't tell his story as plainly as I've related it, but that was the gist. Gramps graciously declined the invitation to help eat the suffocated rooster. We did help Hans prop up enough wreckage to make a crude shelter for the hens, then we went back home.

"Gramps, it looks like we have more damage than Hans. Why do you suppose that is?"

"Well, Boy, wind only does damage when it hits something solid." I waited, but that was all Gramps had to say. He left me to fill in the blank spots myself. Just as well, I guess. I needed a lesson is physics.

Chapter Thirteen

Bronc Riders

One of my ambitions when I was a child was to be a cowboy. I just knew if given a chance that I could be as strong and skillful as Gene Autry or Roy Rogers. My cousin Jerry felt the same way, and he and I often played cowboys when we visited each other.

One of our problems was finding horses to ride. Jerry had some ponies at his farm, and we often rode them, but somehow they didn't present the challenge we needed. However, Gramps had a horse that was just right—Old Rex.

At some time Gramps had wanted an extra work-horse. I don't know what his reason was, but he bought a large gelding from a carload auctioned off in Guthrie Center. This load of horses had come from Wyoming. They were big horses, but most were only broken to saddle. In Wyoming it takes a big strong horse to be able to buck the heavy winter snows. Rex was a big horse.

I don't know how old Rex was when Gramps bought him, but I do know he didn't take to being harnessed. Gramps tried to work him with Bell, the gentle mare, but Rex fought and tangled the harness. After he tore up enough harness and machinery, Gramps gave up—an unusual stance for him—and quit trying to make Rex useful.

Rex was pastured by himself in a small field near the creek. This pasture was not too far from the house, but when the corn was tall it could not be seen. Jerry and I scouted it very well to make sure that was so. We planned to ride Old Rex.

Rex had a lot of saddle marks on his withers and some scars on his shoulders that we couldn't figure out. Later, as a rancher in Oregon, I learned that those marks were the result of spurs. This was a horse that would buck. Rex was a tall, rawboned sorrel, gentle on the ground. He could easily be caught and led, even petted without a problem. However, he took exception to anyone riding him. I'm sure that an experienced rider could have ridden out his pitching and settled him down, but that wasn't really our plan. We liked the pitching and weren't particularly interested in stopping him.

Our biggest problem was that Rex was so tall we could not get on. Of course, we didn't have a saddle —we intended to ride him bareback—so there was nothing to hold onto while trying to climb onto his back, even if Rex would have allowed that. After much discussion, Jerry and I came up with a solution. One of us would lead the horse near a fence post, and the other would climb the post, then jump onto Rex's back. We didn't even think about the danger involved. Since I was oldest by a few months, it was decided that I would ride first.

We caught Rex easily enough and tied a long rope to the halter he always wore. Rex never had his mane trimmed, so it would provide a handhold for the rider. I stood on the other side of the barbed-wire fence while Jerry lead the placid horse near the post we had chosen. When Rex was in position, I climbed the post and stood balanced on the top, then jumped onto Rex's back.

Rex was more startled than frightened, but he reacted as we expected. I had just enough time to grab two fistfuls of long, coarse mane before Rex exploded. I'm sure his pitching wasn't really bad, and he bucked

straight ahead so there was little danger, but it seemed to me that I was on a National Finals Rodeo bronc. I lasted for several seconds, then felt my hands begin to slip. The next thing I knew, I was flying through the air to land on my back with a solid "thump!" By the time I had struggled to my feet, Jerry had Rex under control and was leading him back. The horse was a bit skittish, but he wasn't blowing at all. Jerry was excited, and as he told how high I was thrown and what a picture I made sitting there holding on, I got excited myself. Now it was Jerry's turn.

Once I had led Rex to the fence post, Jerry jumped on and grabbed a handful of mane, and Rex repeated his performance. Young bones usually bend rather than break, and ours bent a lot that day. Neither of us was ever hurt badly. Oh, we got some bruises and scrapes, but we were used to that. We did learn to stay away from our rodeo arena if it had not rained for some time. The ground was just too hard when we landed on it.

Most things that Jerry and I got into were revealed sooner or later. Either one of us let the cat out of the bag or someone else—usually Jerry's little brother, Bobby—told on us. But our wild rides on Old Rex remained our secret. Or at least I always thought so until the day Gramps sold Rex.

It was a sad day for me. Jerry wasn't there to commiserate with me, so I had to bear it all alone. The man who was buying Rex brought a large truck, which he backed up against the manure pile in back of the barn. Gramps led Rex up the pile and into the truck, and Rex was his usual placid self. When Gramps came out of the truck, he must have seen something on my face because he said, "Well, cowboy, better go say goodbye to your horse." He had that twinkle in his eye. As always, Gramps knew more than we thought.

Before Jerry and I thought of riding Old Rex, I had determined to learn to rope like the Cisco Kid. I had twenty feet of one-quarter-inch Manila rope, and Gramps had plaited a hondo on one end for me. I worked with that rope for days on end, finally able to throw it over fence posts and wagon tongues. But that was pretty tame. I needed to find out how good I was with a moving target. Of course, my first thought was to rope Jack, but then when I tried he gave me an injured look and slunk into the wash house.

Next, I decided an arrogant old rooster would be my victim. I spent many minutes stalking him to get close enough, but when I threw the rope, he was gone in a burst of clacking and wing whirr, leaving behind one lonely feather.

I knew that the milk cows and horses were too large to tackle, but we did have a young calf out in the hog pasture. That was it! Just like real cowboys at branding time, I'd be roping a calf.

Now this was a milk-pen calf, which meant that we fed him morning and night. He saw people as his servants—rightly so—and had no fear of us at all. The minute I climbed the fence the calf was headed my way.

I got set, and as soon as he came in range, I began to twirl the loop around my head. That bothered the calf, and he darted away from me. I chased him. Away we went out across the small pasture.

That calf was fast, and while I could run pretty well myself, he was gaining on me. I saw that the time had come to make my cast. One last, hard twirl and out snaked the rope. And wonder of wonders, it settled down over the calf's head like it was supposed to. I pulled back, trying to plant my tennis shoes in the dirt, but unlike high-heeled boots they could find no purchase. The calf not only kept going, he accelerated! I was not about to lose him, so I grimly held on, making long hops and lunges, trying to keep my feet.

We made one full round of the pasture, and I noticed Gramps standing near the fence watching as we came by the hog house. Just there, I lost my footing entirely and went to earth—but I held onto the rope!

The calf was really scared now. He pulled me through the dirt and cockleburs without slowing a bit. I could hear Gramps yelling something, but the words didn't come clear for a second. Then: *"Turn loose of the rope, you fool! turn loose of the rope!"* At last I saw that the battle was lost, and I opened my rope-burned hands and let the calf go.

When I got up I found that the front of my shirt was gone, and I was bleeding from long scratches down my chest and stomach. My hands were bloody where the rope had lacerated them. But my wounds didn't really

hurt too much. After all, I had roped a calf! I turned to the fence and noticed Gramps bent over sort of shaking. When I was close I saw that he was laughing. Tears were running down his face. "Boy, that was the funniest thing I believe I've ever seen. You holding onto that rope and the calf's tail straight up in the air, running for all he was worth!" He stopped to catch his breath, looked me over, and continued, "Are you all right?"

I beamed at him. Was I all right? Why, I was nine feet tall. "Gramps, I roped that calf. I mean I actually roped that calf. I didn't stop him or throw him, and he tore me up a bit, but by golly I roped him!"

Gramps rarely touched me, but he could see how proud I was and he was proud of me. He put his hand on my shoulder and said, "Boy, you sure did. That loop dropped over his head like you'd been roping calves all your life." That hand on the shoulder would have been enough, but for Gramps to praise me, too! I'd never forget this day—and I never have.

Chapter Fourteen

Fishing

August was not my favorite month. Oh, sure, it was still summer, but I knew that when August was over, school would begin. Not only did I not like school, what was worse, I had to move back to town with my mother and sisters. Sure, I had friends that I would be glad to see, but the restrictions of town, the lack of freedom and space, and few really interesting things to do didn't make going back to town a very happy prospect.

Gramps always seemed to know what was bothering me. When he saw me moping around in the first week of August, I guess he knew what was on my mind. I could feel him watching me as I wandered from place to place. Nothing seemed to please me—my BB gun was still propped in the kitchen corner, Jack was off on a hunt by himself, and I had no urge to build a new "wild creation" (Gramps's name for the things I would nail together to play with).

As often happened, Gramps waited until we were milking to make a comment. "Well, Boy, your Uncle Verl called today. Said he was going fishing tomorrow up at Clear Lake. Wanted to know if you would be interested in going along. I told him I wasn't sure, the way you been moping around." He spat a stream of tobacco juice.

I began to get excited. Uncle Verl loved to fish, and he and Aunt Lois often went. They didn't have any children (a subject that the gossips of Guthrie Center liked to turn over) and were free to do what they wanted. I loved to go fishing with them. I always had a lot of fun when I went anywhere with Verl and Lois.

I was learning Gramps's laconic way of speaking. Understatement was the key. "Well, I don't know. I reckon Uncle Verl would be disappointed if I turned him down. I guess I better go."

Gramps spat again. "Now don't force yourself, Boy."

"No, sir, I won't. But I think I ought to go."

Later, from something Aunt Lois said, I learned that Gramps had called Verl to ask him to take me. Gramps was always long on "boyology."

Next morning, very early, Uncle Verl pulled his year-old Ford into the driveway to pick me up. Soon, we were back on the road.

My Uncle Verl takes some explaining. He was a soldier in the Second World War, fighting across Europe. Verl never said much about what happened, except for some funny things, but everybody knew that he saw and took part in some pretty dangerous combat. When Verl returned from the war, he was different. At least that's what I was always told. Verl was not a farmer, but he was an excellent mechanic. That was the trade he chose to follow. He married a girl that didn't exactly fit into his family, though her folks were farmers, too. They were wealthier than our family, and that might have made the difference.

Verl always did what he wanted without asking anyone. And he was willing to pay the price if he made a mistake. Most of the family figured he made a mistake when he married Lois, but if so, he never showed it. He and his wife were happy together. They built a new house, bought good furniture, and generally enjoyed life. I think that was probably what was wrong. In our rural area, people who enjoyed themselves were as suspect as those who snuck off to Penora to buy beer (Guthrie Center was "dry," Penora was "wet"). Yet, Verl was a respected member of the community, a hard worker who was forgiven his strange ideas of "fun."

Arriving back in Guthrie Center, we picked up Aunt Lois and a picnic basket and headed on to Clear Lake. I was happy and excited. Oh, one thing I forgot to tell about Uncle Verl: he was a *fast* driver. He was a good driver, too, but when he hit the open road, the accelerator went down and the telephone poles rushed by so fast they looked like a picket fence. While this frightened some people, I loved it. Except for one little habit that Uncle Verl had. With the speedometer hovering around eighty miles per hour, he would take his hands off the wheel, slowly turn to Aunt Lois, enfold her in a strong embrace, and begin a long, many-second kiss. That scared me! What I couldn't see from the back seat was that he had one eye open and looking down the road, and he was driving with his knee under the steering wheel. He always got the reaction he wanted out of me: "Uncle Verl! Uncle Verl! Look at the road!" Slowly, he would disengage and put his hands back on the wheel. "What's wrong, Junior?" he would drawl in a calm, quiet voice.

The boat we took to Clear Lake was one Uncle Verl had built himself. He had installed a car engine—a Ford 60 V8—in this boat, and it would fly over the water. True, it wasn't exactly a fishing boat, but that didn't bother Verl. We fished for a while, but they weren't biting much. So we reeled in our lines and put out another of Uncle Verl's inventions: a wide board with a rope attached to the front edge for pulling and another rope looped through two holes in the board for a handle.

"Are you ready, Junior?" Uncle Verl called, as I crouched on the board in shallow water.   "Let 'er rip!"

I called in my deepest voice. A roar from the exhaust and the board was jerked away, almost throwing me off. I clung to the hand rope for dear life, and Verl pulled me out across the lake.

Having ridden on the board before with Uncle Verl at the controls, I knew what to expect and looked forward to it with excitement. We made a large, looping circuit of the lake with me beginning to swing the board back and forth across the boat's wake. Then, suddenly, the engine noise changed, and the boat began to fly straight across the lake like an arrow. I knew what was coming and held on tight, following in a straight line.

Just as we were going as fast as I wanted, Verl throttled back and began a sharp turn to the left. As usual, the momentum of the board carried it out past the wake of the boat where it was jerked sharply back into line. I let go of the rope as my feet left the board and sailed out across the water, making a fair dive in my bulky life jacket. I had never yet been able to stay on the board when Uncle Verl pulled "the jerk" on me.

The day ended all too soon. At sunset we loaded the boat back on the trailer and headed home. I slept most of the way, only waking up as we entered Guthrie Center. By the time I was back at the farm I was ready to fall into bed.

August wound down as usual—too fast for me. I tried to pretend that it was really June and that I had a whole summer ahead of me, but that didn't work very well. Finally, the day came when I loaded all of my gear into the '41 Dodge for the trip back to town. I was sad, but not about to cry. Gramps seemed to know how much I wanted to stay, for he was almost conversational as we drove through the countryside, pointing out new fences and ripening corn crops.

When we arrived at our house on 4th Street, my sisters came out to greet me. Mom was at work, and I had that sinking sensation that seemed to accompany all of my summer-end homecomings. Would summer ever come again?

Chapter Fifteen

New Worlds

There was so much to remember on that last visit before I entered the navy. I went around the farm and touched things: the high-sided corn wagon that I had turned into an imaginary stagecoach many times; the "new" chicken house I had helped Gramps build one summer; the water trough under the elm tree, made of a fifty-five-gallon drum laboriously chiseled into two "lengthwise" sections. So many memories.

Gramps was in a talkative mood that night. He let his memory range, talking about his youth and the things he had done—or wanted to do. It slowly dawned on me that he was wishing me well in my adult life. It was a "letting go." By sharing his own dreams—something I had never heard him do before—he was releasing me to manhood. Fortunately it was dark in the room. The tears in my eyes were well hidden.

Later, after I had gone to bed, Grandma came into my room and did something she had not done for many years. She pulled up a straight-backed chair and sat on it, holding my hand. At first we visited about family and things, but then silence, a warm, loving silence settled down. She had come to say goodbye. How I loved her!

I left the next morning to prepare myself for the

U.S. Navy. My mother had remarried and moved with my good stepfather to Fremont, Nebraska, where I had gone to school. I would go there to board a bus for San Diego, California, and bootcamp.

Jack said goodbye to me at the wash house. He was sad, and so was I. I leaned down and hugged him to me, while he whined and licked my face. It suddenly dawned on me that Jack was getting older, too. Then he went into the wash house to crawl under the wood range, his place to hide when things went wrong.

At the car, Gramps put both hands on my arms and looked long into my eyes. He didn't say anything with words, but that look was enough. He put into it all of the love and care he had for me. Then he stood back as I climbed in and closed the door. Grandma was just behind him. "Goodbye, Junior, goodbye! You write to us now. Let us know how you're doing," she said. Gramps spat to the side and gave me that mischievous grin. "You'll do, Boy," was all he said, but it was enough.

I drove slowly away, looking back. They stood and waved as long as they could see me. Gramps knew somehow that I was going into a world he would never know, but he had done all he could to help me be a man. That last "You'll do, Boy" was his send-off. Would I do? Could I measure up to his belief in me? I didn't know. I only knew that I would try.

Chapter Sixteen

Old Jack

I thought about the farm and Gramps and Grandma a lot while I was in the navy. In bootcamp I longed for the peace of those Iowa hills. In the chow hall, I could always close my eyes and see Grandma's wonderful gravy poured over one of her great, huge biscuits, or a slab of her delicious coconut cream pie, so light it almost floated off the plate. It was a sad shock to open my eyes to the greasy beans and tough beef of a navy meal.

When I left bootcamp I went to several schools in the United States, then overseas for a hitch in Japan. Memories of the farm were still there, but not as insistent any longer. Finally, I was assigned to a squadron on the aircraft carrier USS *Bennington* and headed for a cruise in the Far East.

My mom wrote me faithfully, always filling the letters with news of the family, telling me about uncles and aunts, cousins and sisters, nieces and nephews, and of course, Gramps and Grandma and the farm.

The ship was tied up at the dock at Cubi Point Naval Air Station in the Philippines when mail call came on a hot sweaty day. I sat in the scant shade of a helicopter and opened Mom's letter. As usual, it was filled with news. At the end of the letter, Mom added a few words that brought me up short. She wrote: "Oh, yes. Gramps said to tell you, Old Jack died last week."

Those words suddenly surrounded me with memories. I could almost feel Jack's warm, moist dog-tongue rasping across my cheek. Those bright dark eyes and almost-alert ears, his laughing jaws stretched wide in a happy lunatic grin. Why, if I reached out my hand and closed my eyes, surely I would feel his coarse tawny hair slip through my fingers. "Old Jack died last week." Could he really be gone?

The human mind is a funny thing. I hadn't given Jack more than a dozen thoughts for over two years, then along came the letter, and I knew I had lost one of my best friends. I guess Jack had been such a part of the farm that he merged into the memories of all that was good.

There he was in my mind, yipping and jumping around me, trying to hurry me through my chores so we could head for the creek. How we loved to explore that brushy, African, Texas, desert jungle. I was every hero I had seen at the Saturday afternoon picture show—Tom Mix, Gene Autry, Roy Rogers, and Lash Larue all at the same time. Jack was Rin-Tin-Tin and Lassie (I didn't tell him that Lassie was a girl-dog; he was sensitive about those things). And even though he couldn't do all of their tricks, I knew he was just as smart.

We always wondered what breed Jack was. He was a big dog, probably weighing around ninety pounds. He had a shepherd's broad, intelligent head, a collie's long golden hair and white vest, and feet the size of a Great Dane. Jack was a gentle dog, though his bark was ferocious. As related earlier, the only person Jack really seemed to dislike was our dirty neighbor Hans, and we knew that was because of Hans's smell. Hans and how he smelled was about the only area Jack and Grandma agreed on. She'd say, "You don't have to be rich to be clean! Jack didn't fall back on clichés much, but he'd tree Hans every time he got the chance.

Jack had a strong personality that touched everyone, even Grandma. I think she always sort of put up with him until the day of the pancake episode.

My grandmother was a great cook, noted throughout the country for her pies and bread, but like all great people, she had her "fatal flaw." Grandma's pancakes were nearly always a disaster.

Gramps and I came in from chores one cold winter morning, washed up, and seated ourselves at the table. It was Christmas vacation at school, and as always, I wanted to spend as much of it as possible on the farm.

It felt real good sitting next to that old kitchen range. Grandma had it stuffed with corncobs, and it was sending out heat in almost visible waves. I was as ready for breakfast as any growing boy would be who had just spent an hour in the cold doing chores. Then I noticed that Grandma was making pancakes—that dampened my appetite a bit.

The first cakes always seasoned the pans, so they were set aside for the cats. Into the pans poured the batter for the pancakes that would grace our plates. Now boys in my day didn't ever complain about the food they were served. In fact, children rarely spoke at the table unless they were spoken to. Mostly I was content with this situation, but there were times when I wanted to speak my mind; this was one of them, but I managed to keep quiet.

I cut a look at Gramps and noticed the straight

frown line between his eyes that only came at moments of concentration. Grandma slid a warm plate with two large pancakes onto the table. They were moving. Yes, they were, bubbling and kind of heaving like. Gramps reached out a fork and stabbed one of the bubbles. It popped and the skin slowly slid down into the cavity, not a pretty sight. Without a word, Gramps picked up the plate and headed for the door. Grandma and I watched from the window as he scraped the cakes into Jack's pan.

Now I always figured Jack would eat anything that didn't eat him first. I was wrong. His tail was wagging in its usual friendly manner when he first lowered his head to the pan. The wags became slower and slower until they finally stopped. He raised his head and gave Gramps a reproachful look before disappearing into the wash house.

Grandma had two bright spots of red on her cheeks as Gramps came back into the kitchen—could have been from the heat, I suppose. "Mother," he said, "fix us some eggs. If Jack won't eat those cakes, neither will we." Nope, I don't think Grandma ever really forgave Jack for that.

Old Jack. "Old Jack died last week." Maybe. Maybe he died to some, but not to the boy he raised. I'll never watch a dog bring cows down the lane without seeing Jack. Every time I hear high-pitched yelping as dirt flies from a gopher hole, I'll hear Jack. And on rainy days, when I catch the melancholy smell of wetted grass, I'll think of him, lying at my feet, staring out the open door of the wash house at all the things we could do if only the rain would stop. Old Jack will never die to me.

The letter about Jack brought to mind for the first time that Gramps and Grandma wouldn't live forever, either. Still, it was many years after my discharge from the navy when the news came to me in Texas that Grandma had died. I went back for her funeral and saw relatives that I hadn't seen for almost twenty years.

Gramps was very sad, and I only had a few minutes alone with him. We reminisced about the farm, though he had sold it several years before. His memory was sharp, and he even managed to chuckle when we talked about Hans and old Jack. That was the last time I saw Gramps.

A few more years passed. Mom kept me informed of what was happening with the family, as always. Gramps went to live in a nursing home, where he seemed as content as he could be now that Grandma was gone. Then early one morning the phone rang. It was my sister telling me that Gramps was dead. He had died easily at ninety-five years, without a long time in the hospital. My mind grappled with the thought that he was gone, this strong man who was so important in my life.

There was a "blue norther" ice storm blowing in our part of Texas when the funeral took place. Not only could I not get to the airport due to slick and closed roads, but even if I had been able to get there, no flights were going out. I didn't make it to the funeral. I was sorry about that for my mother's sake, but in other ways I didn't mind. I will always remember Gramps as the quiet, authoritative farmer, going about his daily tasks without complaint, passing out bits of wisdom and philosophy, teaching a boy the things he needed to know to make him a man.

There are a lot of clichés in this world to cover life and death situations? I'd like to add another: "Old grandfathers never pass away. They just become even grander in the minds and hearts of those they leave behind." Rest in peace, Gramps.